M000224358

MEDICINE FOR THE TWENTY-FIRST CENTURY

Keith Mason has practised as a radionics practitioner and homoeopath. He worked at the Institute of Complementary Medicine in London, and now has his own flourishing practice, working according to the principles of this book, in Salisbury, Wiltshire, UK. He lectures in the USA, Australia and around the world.

Medicine for the Twenty-First Century

THE KEY TO HEALING WITH VIBRATIONAL MEDICINE

KEITH MASON

ELEMENT

Shaftesbury, Dorset • Rockport, Massachusetts

© Keith Mason 1992

Published in Great Britain in 1992 by
Element Books Limited
Longmead, Shaftesbury, Dorset

Published in the USA in 1992 by
Element, Inc
42 Broadway, Rockport, MA 01966

Cover design by Max Fairbrother
Designed by Roger Lightfoot
Phototypeset by Intype, London
Printed and bound in Great Britain by
Dotesios Ltd, Trowbridge, Wiltshire

British Library Cataloguing in Publication data
Mason, Keith, 1940–
  Medicine for the 21st century : the key to healing with
  vibrational medicine / Keith Mason.
  Includes bibliographical references and index.
  1. Mental healing. 2. Vital force—Therapeutic use.
  3. Alternative medicine. I. Title. II. Title: Medicine
  for the twenty-first century.
  RZ401.M268 1992   615.8′52—dc20   92–10026

Library of Congress Cataloging in Publication data available

ISBN 1–85230–329–8

Contents

List of Figures and Charts and Tables

Acknowledgements

I should like to express my profound gratitude to Chrissie, my dear wife and partner in practice, for all her encouragement, support, ideas and considerable input during our years of research together; to our children, David, Andrew, Louise and Kevin, for giving me space and time; to Michael Mann of Element Books for the encouragement he gave me to write this book; to Peter Morley for his generous financial support during the early years of my research; and to M. Yvon Combe of France for sharing notes and thoughts in the early stages of my work with the blueprint formula.

This book is dedicated to Richard.

Preface

This book, the result of a decade of practical research into the causes of illness and disorder, presents a new biomedical model of humanity. This model evolved out of my studies of Eastern philosophy and my work as a practitioner of complementary medicine using homoeopathy, biochemistry and mineral therapy. My researches led me to the conclusion that, in spite of their superficial contradictions and differences, the sciences of the West and the metaphysical theories of the East shared a common ground from which a systematic approach to healing could be established. In developing such a system, it was not only important for it to be compatible with the different scientific and metaphysical theories of West and East; it also needed to provide an effective method for healing the underlying cause of illness in the individual patient, rather than simply alleviating the visible symptoms.

My added interest in energetic medicine, particularly radionics, led me to develop a system that used numerical coding as a means for establishing a formula that represented the various aspirations, strengths, and weaknesses of my patients at a causative level.

This formula of ten elemental categories evolved over approximately ten years and was finally established as a true and workable equation for an individual's own vital essence. The concept is based upon insight into the more hidden elements of Theosophy, Qabalistic numerology and Eastern philosophy in general, with comparisons between certain diseases and symptoms and patient types.

It was established that certain patient types displayed similar symptoms, mental and emotional characteristics, attitudes and desires, and similar cosmological vibrations and hereditary backgrounds. It was evident when making these comparisons that certain information provided by the patients gave details of a pre-existence, or blueprint, of physical strengths and weaknesses, a predisposition to certain symptoms, and tangible evidence of a purpose to their lives. It was obvious to me that a formula was hidden somewhere within these subtle correspondences, perhaps of a numerical nature.

The Greeks sought to create all manner of ratios and harmonies with numbers which they believed resonated throughout the universe. Pythagoras, who discovered the diatonic scale, also believed this. The diatonic scale is the basis of much of the world's music, all of which is produced as harmony and melody by simple numerical ratios, particularly when dealing with string lengths and vibrations.

It was during this century that a theoretical physicist, Eugene Wigner, suggested that attention be given to what he called the unreasonable effectiveness of mathematics. Again and again, abstract and beautiful relationships, explored for their own aesthetic sake, are later found to have exact correspondences with the real world; a coincidence which is quite remarkable.

Systematically, by experimenting with numerical ratios and values together with patient information, the final formula of ten elemental categories was developed, albeit over many years and with many adaptations. In the course of my practice I found that a comparison between this formula and the symptoms displayed by individual patients gave me a great insight into the true cause of their various illnesses and, subsequently, into their healing.

In a world where matters of health and well-being are of as much concern to the general public as they are to those engaged in the various medical and health care professions, I hope that this book and the ideas it contains will be of interest to the lay reader as well as to my professional colleagues in the world of medicine and healing.

I should like to express my sincere thanks to my good friend and co-writer John Baldock for the part he played in writing the finished manuscript and for the profound contribution he made to the book in the process.

Keith Mason

Introduction

In recent decades there have been some very dramatic changes in the fundamental principles governing medicine. For more than a century, these principles were inspired by the laws related to energy and matter established by Newton some 300 years ago, as a result of which the human body was considered to function mechanically, rather like a clockwork model, according to determinable physical principles. Such a model largely ignored the possible influence of mind and consciousness on the functioning of the human body – an attitude that was reflected in the approach to the medicine of the time. Because the human body was primarily regarded as a material or physical object, the medical treatment of illness and disease was essentially material or physical in nature, relying on drugs, surgery, irradiation or similarly material-based systems.

Nonetheless, these forms of medical treatment represented a significant advance in the history of healing and it was understandable that for many, the future of medicine and medical research was seen as lying entirely in this direction. However, the development of psychiatry as a branch of medicine and the growing consideration given to the role of psychological factors in illness and disease was to initiate a period of further change and development, during which the dimension of 'mind' was added to the physical body. For the first time, scientific medicine examined the idea of mind and consciousness causing change at a physical level. Medical science began to recognize that the emotions, hypersensitivity, and mental attitudes had material effect upon the physical body. The last two or three decades have seen further recognition of this relationship between the functioning of the mind and the physical body as certain physical symptoms such as heart conditions, cancer and hypertension, have been shown to be influenced to some degree by the mind.

This same period has witnessed the evolution of complementary medicine, with doctors and practitioners combining aspects of allopathic (conventional) medicine with the techniques of meditation and relaxation as well as disciplines practised by other health care professionals such as homoeopathy, acupuncture, hypnotherapy, and so on. Possibly the most significant impact on developments in this area, and one which had previously been absent from the field of conventional medical practice, was the recognition given to *the power of the mind* and its potential role in healing the body.

Once again, it would seem as though medicine has reached its ultimate form – this time in the age of mind/body medicine. Is it possible to go beyond this? I believe it is. Just as we have seen a purely material approach to medicine replaced by one which largely attributes the cause and cure of physical disease to the mind, I believe that the medicine of the twenty-first century will go beyond the two dimensions of 'body' and 'mind' to recognize a further, third dimension: a casual dimension to the mind. In other words, it will take into account a possible *purpose* to life itself.

This causal dimension lies beyond our conventional understanding of space and time and is part of what is sometimes referred to as the 'universal mind'. A similar idea is encountered in modern physics – whilst classical physics expressed its understanding of the unity of the universe in mechanistic terms, as a machine, quantum physics likens it more to a vast thought process or mind. In the present context, the human mind should not be regarded solely as a localized, individual phenomenon, functioning independently within each and every human being. It has a causal dimension which is part of the supreme universal mind that 'thinks' itself into material being through the subtle energy fields that give existence to the physical body. In other words, the causal dimension operates through what we might call the realms of 'antimatter' or 'thought form' before materializing in the physical world as 'matter'.

The underlying principle of three-dimensional medicine is that we take into account this causal dimension of the mind as the initial element in the sequence of cause (or purpose) → mind → physical body. Our examination of the relevance for medicine of this causal dimension will bring together identifiable factors from the universal mind and known aspects of the human body. In so doing we will consider the body and its life span, its individual thought forms and attitudes (including those inherited genetically or acquired from other sources), and the development of the subtle energy fields surrounding the physical form.

Left to her own devices, nature lives totally at one within the realms of a universal order that is as predictable as tomorrow's rising sun, the seasons and the pathways of the heavenly bodies. Humankind, existing within the realms of this same universal order, should also be able to live in peace and harmonious union with it, sharing in the progressive unfolding of an evolutionary process. However, instead of sharing in this universal order, we tend to strive for egoistic fulfilment, thus producing disorder and disease in both humanity and the natural world.

Our awareness of the order inherent in the visible and invisible worlds has recently been increased by the observations of the 'new' biologists and physicists; at the same time, quantum theory has given us the uncertainty and chaotic principles. Recent research has also shown us that the outcome of experiments can be influenced by the mind and projected thoughts of the observer, thus indicating that we, as observers, have the potential to influence not only the unfolding of our own destiny but also that of our planet and perhaps, to a somewhat lesser degree, that of the universe. The nature of this influence becomes increasingly apparent when we consider that the order existing in the natural world can be turned into disorder through the mind and its projection of disorderly or 'incorrect' thought forms.

Similarly, by attuning ourselves to the power of the universal mind and the harmonious order it projects on the universe, it is possible for us to recognize the disorder in our planetary environment and to heal it through the restoration of order. Medical practice has shown that it is also possible to heal humans and animals through the corrective influence of the mind and its projected thoughts. For us to explore this potential for healing within the universal order, the traditional medical or biophysical model of man as an individual mechanism needs to be replaced by a new model that incorporates these additional universal dimensions.

The formulation of such a model is at present hampered by the strong divisions that traditionally segregate allopathic from complementary medicine, physics from metaphysics, biology from cosmology, and science from religion. The new knowledge emerging in such fields as physics and biology is, however, moving towards the recognition of a common ground or centre in which it is increasingly apparent that all systems (whether of a physical or metaphysical nature) come together and meet each other. It is at this centre or meeting point that we encounter the blueprint or matrix for the life of the human organism which provides the potential formula for our new model.

This blueprint emanating from the universal mind is identifiable in each and every one of us, and is unique for each individual human life. Our understanding of its formulation has significant implications for the future of medicine, as it may provide doctors and practitioners with a broader insight into the diagnosis of the underlying causes of illness and disease. At the same time, it offers physical and metaphysical medicine the potential to heal illness and disease within the blueprint by healing the patient's mind and physical body and giving direction to that patient for their own evolution within the universal order.

In this book, the setting and subsequent unfolding of the blueprint will be explored by tracing the life of the individual human organism from conception onwards, through its goals and ambitions and its predisposition to certain illnesses. The course of this setting and unfolding is affected by the interplay of numerous energetic forces which, in acting through the various subtle bodies as well as the physical body, combine to form the whole individual. The continued good health of the individual as a whole depends upon the maintenance of a harmonious balance between these different energetic forces – and this balance has the potential to be sustained or regulated through the energetic elements of allopathic and complementary medicine. The methods of diagnosis and treatment this involves will be illustrated with case histories and the results of the methods used in restoring health. We shall also examine the role of the individual's own consciousness in facing illness or maintaining good health.

The potential medical model proposed in this book provides a formula of individual causation and a workable principle for treatment. The treatment instruments now available that use this principle (see p.137) provide a system of energetic medicine which may either be taken orally by the patient or used in a space-time quantum to treat the patient by balancing the mind-body with the causal dimension. It is my belief that it is the latter, the causal or third dimension, which is the dimension to be explored in developing a medicine for the future.

CHAPTER 1

A Model From Conception

In exploring a model to replace the now outdated mechanical concept of humanity, we must first determine the elements of creativity existing within the human form – for example, the creative relationships between antimatter and matter (the pre-physical realm and the physical form), and the individual cell and the whole individual. As the physical body develops from its causation in the formative energy fields to maturity, it is continually influenced by these same causal fields and by thought forms of a more tangible nature. There are also clearly definable attitudes and aspirations to be documented for each individual at the level of personality. Furthermore, in formulating our model we should be able to show the influence of the causal dimension and these various thought forms upon the physical form.

These are some of the elements that will help us construct the blueprint for our model. The first of them to consider is the relationship between matter and antimatter – the physical and pre-physical dimensions of existence.

MATTER AND ANTIMATTER

Matter, as such, may assume many forms but by its very nature it also has recognizably finite limitations. In necessarily broad terms, we can say that matter assumes two easily distinguishable categories of form. The one corresponds with the established laws of physics and chemistry and includes chemical compounds, elements and certain mixtures; the other is caused by an external influence. Ice provides us with a useful illustration of both these categories. On the one hand, the formation and components of ice correspond to recognizable physical and chemical laws; on the other, the actual shape assumed by a block of ice can be influenced by an external cause – for example, a sculptor.

How do we regard the human form in relation to these two categories?

The formation of elements or compounds occurs for known physical or chemical reasons – for example, hydrogen and oxygen have a natural inclination to form water and, if suitable conditions prevail, they will form ice. But are these elements and their natural inclinations themselves influenced by a causal element of the universal mind? How far can we assume that inorganic matter is truly *inorganic*? Organic, living forms appear to be influenced by a further causation and are built according to genetic instructions. Pure matter, as elements and minerals, has no inclination to produce the human form any more than it has the innate inclination to produce a piece of furniture or a television set.

Matter has to be instructed how to produce the human form and the various known forms of the animal and vegetable kingdoms, cell by cell, protein by protein, via the genetic code. Although matter may assume innumerable organic forms, it can be said that, of itself, it is indifferent to those forms. It could therefore be suggested that organic forms are not produced solely as a physical or chemical necessity, as is the case with compounds and elements – although, regarding the latter, it must be said that the forms produced by their innate inclination are rather limited.

Here again, in the same way that there is an apparent link between the universal mind and a causal mind in the human form, there also appears to be a causal element affecting both inorganic and organic matter. However, human and animal forms with their accompanying energy systems and mental ability transcend all other natural forms, not only because of their specialized abilities and their unique place within the universal order, but also because an explanation for the cause of their existence lies beyond the currently recognized laws of physics and chemistry.

What does produce them? What cause lies behind the genetic

code of the DNA and the production of animal and plant species? Furthermore, how can we explain the additional dimensions of individuality, personality, culture, desire and ambition within the human form? Matter alone cannot be the cause, for matter itself has no inclination to produce these forms or to generate individual differences in human consciousness or awareness.

If for a moment we consider an engineer or a mason as being the creator or cause of a material form – that is, a form consisting of matter – and that the machine or building he produces is the material conclusion of an idea in the mind of its creator, then perhaps, by extension, we may ask the question, 'Is there a creative mind that shapes elements into compounds and inorganic matter?' Or, alternatively, 'Is there a creative mind that shapes matter into organic forms, including the human form?' Perhaps the same idea can also be expressed in more scientific terms: 'Does energy create matter, or does matter create energy?'

One of the first scientists to experiment with the effects of electric and magnetic forces was Michael Faraday (1791–1867). Making the forces themselves, rather than the effect they produced, the primary object of his research, he went beyond the accepted theories of Newtonian physics by replacing the concept of force with the more subtle concept of force fields. He also recognized the influence of a causal factor. Faraday showed that force fields had their own reality and could be studied without reference to a material body. This was the beginning of electrodynamics and subtle causation. In the same century, the theory of electromagnetism was evolved by James Clerk Maxwell (1831–1879) who showed that light was in fact a rapidly alternating electro-magnetic field travelling through space in the form of waves.

By the early 1930s, the physicists of the day believed they had grasped the 'stuff' of which matter, the world and the universe were made. This was the four elementary particles, the electron, proton, neutron and photon, plus the force fields of gravity and electromagnetism. Atoms were found to have a central nucleus made up of protons and neutrons, surrounded by one or more orbital electrons. The protons were shown to carry a positive electrical charge and electrons a negative one, making the whole atom electrically neutral. The unique chemical properties of each atom were defined by the then known quantum physical arrangement of electrons in different energy states. This exclusive phenomenon made each atom unique. So, at the beginning of the 1930s, nature had given up its secrets and physicists had found the basic building blocks from which all matter was formed. Or had they?

THE GENETIC CODE

In the 1950s, Watson and Crick discovered the double-helix structure of DNA (deoxyribonucleic acid), the elongated code-bearing molecule in the cell chromosomes which contains and transmits genetic information. The genetic code or 'language' consists of four basic 'letters', each of which relates to one of the four nitrogenous bases (adenine, cytosine, guanine and thymine) of DNA. A sequence of three of these bases, known as a triplet, forms the 'code' for one of the twenty different amino acids which, in turn, go to make up the all-important proteins. These four bases or letters of the genetic 'code' therefore represent the matter, the building blocks, of life itself. The significance of the possible number of triplets – sixty-four ($4 \times 4 \times 4 = 64$) – will be explained later.

Of profound importance is the fact that all living organisms are composed of different permutations and combinations of just twenty amino acids. On their own, the basic amino acids have no biological properties – they are considered inorganic – but join them together to form proteins and they become the very essence and causation of life. The fact that all living things share this essential life-generating core is thought-provoking. Could it be that these living forms are also permeated by a causation of another kind – that of the universal mind? In unravelling the genetic structure, Francis Crick remarked that biology had gone full circle, and yet there was still no explanation as to *why* a wounded organism should recreate its structure and functions exactly as they had existed before it was damaged.

The codes locked up in the chromosomes of all living organisms have the same chemical substance and use the same code script. Within each organism, the genetic information contained in one cell is thought to be identical with that contained in each and every other cell. What then causes cells to specialize? How do cells know that they should become muscle cells, lung cells, and so on? Questions such as these perhaps explain why there is today a groundswell of opinion among many biologists which holds that molecular biology may be reaching its limits.

The seventeenth-century philosopher Descartes declared that the laws of mechanics applied to nature: that the matter of man, animals and all living things was mechanistic. He saw no need to examine conscious awareness to explain human behaviour or to account for the development of illness. As a result of this attitude, biology explained illness purely as a breakdown of parts at a physical/chemical level – a view still held by many physicians today, and visible in the massive amounts of chemical drugs prescribed in medical practice.

The shortcomings of the mechanistic concept also affect the approach traditionally adopted by biologists. Through it, we may have learnt the precise structure of a few genes, but what is known of the way genes communicate and cooperate in the development of an organism? Less than 5 per cent of the genetic code is used to determine specific proteins in the life chain – what of all the other activity integrated in the total DNA code? Surely a 'new' biology needs to recognize the existence of intelligence and thought processes within cellular structures? At the same time, perhaps it also needs to recognize the possible existence of a causal factor that promotes the formation of proteins from permutations of amino acids.

From what we have said so far, it begins to look as though matter does not need special instructions to produce water or snow flakes. These inorganic forms exist because of the latent chemical capabilities of their components. The same cannot be said of organic forms. In this connection we can reasonably state that the exact nature of the genetic code is as important for biology as the periodic table of the elements is for chemistry. There is one important difference, however. The periodic table would be the same throughout the universe. The genetic code, although using the predictable sixty-four triplets mentioned earlier, appears to have an additional dimension – a mind of its own.

In our earlier reference to a block of ice, we showed how its final form was caused by an external influence – in that particular instance, a sculptor. To extend the analogy, we can say that the mind of an artist, or some other person, is the causation of a material form, even though the final form may be manufactured by a machine. By further extension, we may also consider the existence of a mind or energetic intelligence that directs and shapes matter into organic forms, possibly even creating chemical mechanisms to produce the final form. It is here that we encounter the most profound mystery of life – the possible existence of a *divine spark* or *will*, the very essence of life itself, operating within and throughout the natural world.

CELLS

It appears that the sequence of 'mind into matter' governs the intercellular relationship of the millions of cells that together constitute the matter of human form – for example, when part of the delicate human organism is damaged, some form of central intelligence is aware that additional help is required in repairing the damaged cells.

How is it that cells are able to communicate with each other throughout the whole organism? Could it be that a mind factor exists both in the organism as a whole and in the individual cell? If this is the case, it seems reasonable to conclude that medicine can no longer approach the human form according to the mechanical model. The human body is not a machine. A machine such as the motor car contains parts that affect the performance of other parts but, when all is said and done, one wheel cannot produce another wheel. The constituent parts of a machine exist *for* one another, not *because of* each other. The cause that produces a wheel is not to be found in the nature of wheels but outside it, in a causal mind which puts the thought or idea of a wheel into effect. The effect or result, as we see it, is the material form of the wheel. The cause exists before the effect – and with the non-mechanical human model, the cause that produces cells is seen to be within the cells themselves.

The human form consists of billions of cells, all originating from one fertilized egg. What occurs at fertilization to set in motion the production of these billions of variably functioning cells which continue to be self-reproducing? Generally speaking, each of these cells is capable of division and self-reproduction, but what differing energetic exchanges or computations determine whether a cell can or cannot reproduce? And if human cells are capable of self-reproduction, what determines whether the reproduction process can take place within or without the human form?

As we know, it requires two people – male and female – to produce another person, a child. One individual human being, although made up of many self-reproducing cells, cannot of itself reproduce another human being. For one reason or another, however, a small number of people – both male and female – are unable to produce children. Nevertheless, it is obvious that they themselves are a living form made up of self-reproducing cells. While the reproduction of another living form may not always be possible, cellular self-reproduction within the original form is not only possible but is essential in order to maintain normal growth and repair. This ability to self-repair is an absolute necessity for the continuance of a living form. Without this ability, the form would not exist long enough to be regarded as *living*.

When discussing the genetic code, it was mentioned that the encoded information is regarded as being identical in each cell. How is it, then, that cells are able to specialize in a number of different ways? Here again, we confront questions regarding variations in the development of individual organisms that emphasize the limitations of the mechanistic approach to the · human model. In seeking an answer to these questions, we once more encounter the profound mystery that lies beneath the surface of life. The variations in the formation and behaviour of cells (as we saw above with matter) lead us towards a point where we can only conclude that the causation of these variations must lie in a subtle, but immensely powerful, unseen energy.

FIELD THEORIES

A brief reference was made earlier to the work done by Faraday on subtle force fields. Subtle fields cause action at a distance – that is, objects such as charged particles (for example, magnets or human body cells) are able to affect each other in spite of the physical gap that separates them. Field theory is now one of the fundamental concepts in physics and, according to quantum theory, particles (in other words, the matter from which material objects are formed) are themselves manifestations of these fields.

Quantum theory has also shown us that formed matter cannot be effectively analysed as a series of independent and isolated elements. One may refer to causal laws in physics and biology but the notion of separate parts, such as atoms or subatomic particles, is an idealization with (literally) little solidity. We cannot predict events occurring in the subatomic world of matter with any certainty; we can only predict their probability. This does not mean that events of this nature, taking place in the unseen world within matter, occur in an arbitrary or haphazard fashion. It means that they are not provoked by local causes. It is here that we encounter the mystery of a causal mind of universal order, for the behaviour of any one part, whether wave-form or particle, is determined by its interconnectedness with the whole. And since physics has no 'whole', the role of a universal mind has to be seriously considered.

In classical mechanics, the properties and functions of the parts determine the function of the whole. According to quantum theory, the situation is reversed: the whole determines the behaviour of the parts. Therefore, in exploring an alternative to the mechanistic human model, we should include an examination of the role of the fields that affect the particles within human cells. Quantum theory (which will be expanded upon in later chapters) makes use of comparisons between quantum processes and thought processes. In this area, there is some degree of consensus amongst modern physicists regarding a non-mechanical reality, in that the universe begins to seem more like a great thought process than a great mechanical process.

Similarities between the structure of matter and the structure of mind should not surprise us too much. Metaphysics has long regarded the subtle fields of energy surrounding matter as having a causal dimension related to the universal mind. Similarly, the whole of the universe is seen to affect the individual parts within it and, likewise, the whole of the individual human is considered to affect the parts (organs, cells, etc.) within the human form . . . but more of this later.

A crucial feature of field and quantum theory is the role attributable to the observer. Not only is the observer necessary to observe the properties of any atomic phenomenon; paradoxically, he or she is also necessary in order to bring about these properties. For example, a conscious decision to observe an electron will, to some extent, determine the properties of the electron. If the observer poses a wave-form question, they will receive a wave-form answer; if they pose a particle question, they will receive a particle answer. The minute electron does *not* have properties independent of the mind of the observer. We can no longer speak of mechanistic divisions between mind and matter, between the observer and the observed. We cannot even speak about the world of nature and the universe without simultaneously speaking about ourselves.

In considering a possible new model of humanity we have examined the role of matter, including cells and particles with their attendant fields of electromagnetic forces. In order to develop this new model further, we need to expand upon the relationship between matter and antimatter, the physical and pre-physical. As quantum physics refers to thought form and the influence on matter, it should be possible in constructing our model to draw together some of the parallel ideas that exist in physics and metaphysics.

CONCEPTION

Are mind and matter produced by the coming together of two different form of energy? What transpires within mind and matter to cause self-reproduction?

It is possible to reproduce certain cells outside the body. Certain chemistry exists that can duplicate various cells but not the entire human form, even though the matrix of the DNA code, amino acids and proteins of living matter are all known factors. The female egg may be fertilized by the male sperm yet the reproduction process of cell division will not necessarily progress towards implantation on the uterine wall. There has to be an added element: the mind element, or antimatter, which we can also refer to as *purpose* or *will*.

A degree of this mind element must exist within all cells to enable the specialization that takes place. The mind element apparent at the point of conception is perhaps best described as a spark of that spiritual and mysterious energy that is written about in many metaphysical texts.

How did you or I develop from one single cell? This central question involves, and will, I believe, continue to retain, an element of mystery. Nonetheless, as humanity continues along its evolutionary path, we are learning more of the secrets that lie concealed behind this mystery, some of which are essential in formulating a new biological model.

The human embryo is a self-contained entity. During the first stage of its existence, known medically as the pre-embryo, it grows from a single cell to thirty-two cells. The cells of the pre-embryo have no specialized qualities. In fact, at this stage, there is no clear distinction between those cells that will develop into the foetus and those that will go on to form the placenta and other supporting tissues. Medically, this early stage of development is termed 'non-individual' and it is not yet certain that this tiny ball of cells will develop into a foetus. Perhaps no foetus will develop – or perhaps one, even two or more, may result.

At conception, when the female egg is fertilized by the male sperm, the embryo is little more than a large single cell. Within this cell are the two pronuclei, the small structures that carry the hereditary genes of the parents. The transitional process from cell to foetus begins when the two pronuclei fuse to form the nucleus of the cell. What happens at this point of fusion? Is there an additional dimension, a mind element or perhaps even a divine spark, that causes the pronuclei to fuse together? Does an element of *purpose* cause the innate characteristics of individual differentiation to fuse with the pronuclei? We shall return to these questions later when we consider the possible origins of antimatter – for the present, we go back to the 'matter' we were discussing.

The matter in this instance is now a single-celled embryo or zygote which begins to divide purposefully. The process of sub-division that takes place at this early stage is known as cleavage – each cell simply divides to form two more identical cells; the single cell divides to form two cells, the two divide to form four, and so on. Cleavage continues for approximately three days after fertilization until a ball of thirty-two cells has been formed and then dramatic changes begin to occur. The cells start to organize themselves. At the thirty-two cell stage, the individual blueprint of life begins to emerge.

Between days three and five, the cells continue to organize

themselves, forming inner and outer cells. The outer cells (tro-phectodes) will form the placenta and other supporting tissues; the inner cell mass will go on to form the embryo proper. At day six, the cells of the placenta and the inner mass of the embryo begin the implantation process. The inner cell mass burrows through the outer membrane that has protected the last six days of inner activity and implants itself on the uterine wall. The development of the foetus to a set plan, containing the desired genes for a specialized individual, is now inevitable. The blueprint is set and intervention by external genetic influ-ence is now impossible. The case of test-tube babies, however, does demonstrate that intervention is possible prior to the six-day stage.

Test-tube babies evolve from the manipulation of young embryos in the laboratory. The process involves the female receiving hormone drugs to stimulate the production of more than one mature egg in the monthly cycle. These eggs are retrieved by a catheter and fertilized with the male sperm in a laboratory dish. Once the pronuclei fuse and first cleavage has occurred, the young embryo is placed in the uterus. If conditions are favourable, implantation will result; however, it appears that implantation will not occur once the embryo has developed beyond the six-day stage. It would therefore appear that the number of cells at the six-day stage (i.e. thirty-two) is an impor-tant factor in the successful implantation of the developing human embryo.

In animal experimentation, genetic engineers are able to pro-duce hybrid animals. For example, experiments mixing a four-cell sheep embryo with an eight-cell goat embryo have produced an animal which is both sheep and goat: the *geep*. The moral and practical value of such experimentation may be question-able, but it is quoted here to illustrate what can be done before the six-day stage of embryo development has elapsed. The reader will probably be familiar with the idea of the human *clone* – an identical copy of a human being, produced artificially by cell manipulation. In theory, a single cell, removed from an adult body, is implanted into a one-cell embryo which has had its own nucleus removed. The development of the embryo from then on is controlled by the genes of the adult cell, producing a copy or clone of the adult. Genetic research has shown, however, that crucial genes controlling development are switched off in adult cells – and yet cells within the adult body are continually reproducing themselves and regenerating damaged tissue. In fact, they are capable of reproducing the whole body over a six-month period, which is the life span of certain cells within the body. Why then do genetic engineers find that the process is impossible at the embryo stage? Is it because antimatter or the mind element (or even the divine purpose) influences the outcome, outweighing material predominance?

This last point brings us to examine the possible influence of antimatter in the six-day period during which the young embryo develops from one single cell and, at the same time, to consider its influence on the whole life of the individual human being.

ANTIMATTER AND THE UNIVERSAL MIND

Possibly one of the most baffling things about biological organisms is their teleological quality – in other words, the possible existence of a causal element that provides an ultimate purpose in their development. Final causation as a motivating force behind biological development has enjoyed little credibility with orthodox medicine and science. The mystery surrounding living organisms with regard to possible antimatter properties has been shunned, and science has merely suggested that living organisms and systems represent a class apart: a form of matter and energy that is so strange that it defies the laws governing 'ordinary' matter and energy.

Homoeopathy uses the term *vital essence* to describe this mysterious vitality or energy that provides the causal element in living organisms. Most modern alternative therapies and treatments recognize the presence of some form of energetic causation within all living forms. All living beings, so it appears, share the fundamental characteristic of being endowed with purpose – a purpose which is accomplished by its realization through the living organism. Perhaps this sense of purpose enables us to regard living organisms as the supreme example of active matter having a causation in antimatter or the universal mind. Living organisms are endowed with many other characteristics – growth, adaptability, variety, increasing complexity and, of course, unpredictability. In addition, human organisms are characterized by mental and emotional states. But what of the underlying purpose, the causal factor?

The most challenging question for science and medicine today must be (and perhaps always has been), '*What* is life?' Is it possible that a blueprint for the complete individual – an image in the mind of the Creator, so to speak – exists in advance of the organism? And in advance of implantation?

There must be a point at which 'life' begins for the fertilized egg. When fertilization takes place, does the blueprint or plan of action exist – not only to arrange the chemical processes, but also for the organism's physical and mental states relative to its purpose and aspirations for this lifetime?

The billions of cells that make up the individual human form develop from a single cell and the fusion of the pronuclei. It is not unreasonable to suggest that the further cleavage of cells to the thirty-two cell stage and the subsequent implantation have a purpose and goal; that is, they adhere to a blueprint. It is at this point that we should consider the mysterious *endergonic process* and its operation within the cells of the organism. According to the medical dictionary, the *endergonic process* is the absorption or input of free energy; but free energy from where?

Free energy exchange between cells takes place at all stages of development in the human organism, from embryo to adult. This exchange of energy, or endergonic process, must include the 'energies' of purpose, thought and memory. The reason for this is perhaps self-explanatory when we consider that certain brain cells are renewed within six months, while others die off completely. Memory must therefore exist at an energetic or anti-matter level, rather than a purely material level, which leads us to regard the mind as non-localized. Thought is actually free energy, and the thought process can be related to the endergonic process.

Earlier, we referred to the comparisons that quantum theory draws between quantum processes and thought processes. There are also similarities between structures of mind and structures of matter which lead us to consider thought processes as the structure of antimatter – that is, as a field of *ideas* containing the purpose and goal of the living organism. It may be that a similar field (possibly 'divine' in nature) exists as the universal mind.

In the words of Sir James Jeans, the English astronomer and physicist:

> The concepts which now prove to be fundamental to our understanding of nature . . . seem to my mind to be structures of pure thought . . . the universe begins to look more like a great thought than a great machine.

This suggests that the universe is brimming over with live thought; that thought is not confined to the brains of individual organisms, and that there exists a universal mind or order, unrestrained by time and space. It was also suggested earlier that the material element within the genes of the organism was not a controlling factor, and that organisms had a mind of their own. Furthermore, there must be a thought origin to the organism, and a structure of thought management behind the individual organism's purpose and goal. In looking for the source from which these thought processes and structures originate, we should perhaps turn to the universal mind.

Is it possible that the act of thinking does not of itself produce thought? To put this another way, is there a level of thought that already exists, and we merely tune our non-localized mind to receive thoughts emanating from a universal source? Such an explanation would account for individuals picking up the same thoughts at the same time, even when miles apart. The fact that thought transcends space and time demonstrates that our minds are non-localized; and that the mind is not focused solely within the confines of our physical body. Similarly, the mind element within our cells could be deemed a manifestation of the universal mind. We are then as much a product of this mind element within our cells as we are of the universal mind that governs our individual destiny within humanity as a whole.

What is this universal mind? Is it the same *divine spark* or *purpose* spoken of in so many philosophical texts? Is it possible to begin to unravel the thought structures within the divine purpose that cause the fusion of the pronuclei – the active process that begins the life of the human form? Perhaps it is possible to shed some light on the intelligent thought form of the universal mind by combining quantum theory with aspects of metaphysics. In approaching the concepts of new physics through the traditional theories of metaphysics, it may be possible to construct a framework of tangible thought form apparent within the mind element of cells. Of crucial importance to the structure of this framework is the endergonic process – the exchange of free energy in the transmission of thought from cell to cell – directed by the mitochondria in each living cell.

PHYSICS AND METAPHYSICS

If a purpose (whether divine or otherwise) to human form does exist, as well as a blueprint for the life of the individual, where do they come from? How do they manifest themselves? Are they the combination of two separate energies, constituted by mind and matter?

It was suggested earlier that the possible production of human form does not rest within the mind of matter alone, nor, as far as we can assume, in the pre-physical realms of antimatter. Perhaps it is a combination of both, with the addition of a spark or purpose from the divine mind of universal order. It is here that we enter the realms of metaphysical and philosophical theory. For example, ancient religious traditions speak of the influence of the soul, and its choice at conception of a particular blueprint and purpose. Similar traditions affirm the divine nature of the universal mind, source of the causal mind element at conception and the fusion of the pronuclei – the divine spark of universal mind energy that sets the pattern of cleavage to the thirty-two cell stage prior to implantation. I believe that here we find a clue to the unravelling of the blueprint for the individual: in certain metaphysical texts the same number, thirty-two, is used in connection with energies and thought forms pertaining to the *Tree of Life* (see p. 26).

Of course, there are many complex issues to be addressed when discussing subatomic structures and their various abilities, and the same is true for the paradoxical world of antimatter and its spiritual connections. To avoid overcomplicating these issues, let us assume that three basic dimensions of activity exist at the levels of both matter and antimatter. These are:

1. Purpose
2. Thought
3. Action

These three dimensions come together simultaneously in a living organism to create the following scenario: the individual life of the organism (the purpose) requires a divine spark from the universal mind (the thought) to draw together the attributes of both matter and antimatter (the action). The combination of these three dimensions forms the whole organism, including a dimension we might call the *soul*.

THE DIMENSIONS OF LIFE

As we continue to explore the different energies and dimensions that are connected with the individual organism, it is an appropriate moment to establish some form of visual frame of reference. This is provided by Figures 1, 2 and 3, which symbolize the dimensions of matter and antimatter and the activity leading to the fusion of the pronuclei. The numbers and explanations accompanying the diagrams are important as they will be used throughout the later chapters of the book when calculations are made from the formulae (also provided later) to determine the individual identity within the blueprint.

The numbers used in Figure 1 are derived from the numerical values occurring in Tibetan medicine and theosophical practice, as well as the numbers they attribute to certain energy centres and glands.

The two equilateral triangles symbolize the forces attributed to antimatter and matter. The upper triangle, with the points marked 2, 3, 4, and 1 at the central point, represents the vast amount of information related to the power of purpose, thought and action. This information will be expanded in Chapter 2 with an explanation of all the tangible thought forms, actions and attributes associated with the various numbers. For the moment, it is sufficient to establish the following points:

1 = Spiritual purpose and will
2 = Love and wisdom
3 = Higher active intelligence
4 = Harmony out of sacrifice or conflict

The lower triangle, marked 5, 6, 7, with 8 at the central point, represents the material realm and the more physical activities associated with it:

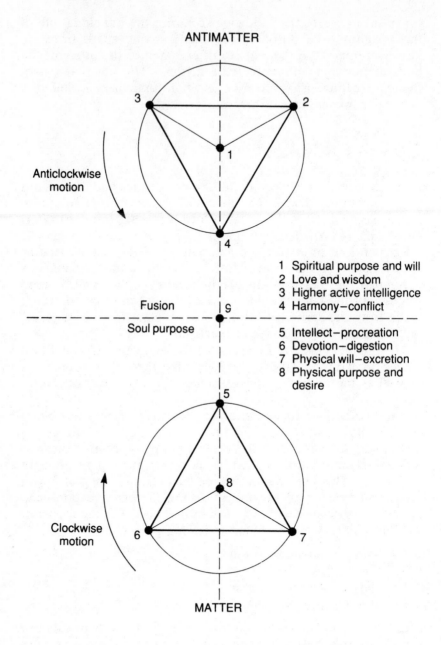

Figure 1   The forces of matter and antimatter

5 = Intellect and procreation
6 = Devotion and digestion
7 = Physical will and excretion
8 = Physical purpose and desire

Number 9, at the point of fusion, represents the amalgamation of matter and antimatter, the fusion of the pronuclei and the soul purpose.

All nine numbers and their manifestations are bi-polar in the sense that they have both a physical and a thought form. All matter, and here we include the developing foetus, comprises elemental particles, or as modern physics suggests 'Super Strings'.

The Super String theory burst upon the scientific world in 1984, and suggested that the building blocks of the universe, including living matter (i.e. protons, neutrons and electrons) are not elementary particles, as had long been thought, but rather tiny massless strings that vibrate at a specific frequency and twist or rotate in ten dimensional space.

The metaphysical view of the Super String theory has not been investigated as far as I am aware, however I perceive the theory as analogous to the subtle meridian theory I have used in my research since 1984. These energetic meridians flowing through the electromagnetic force fields of the individual cells and around the body as a whole have been documented in the book as *Daath* or 0, and the 9 energy or thought centres, and their attendant twenty-two subtle meridians or thought strings.

The nine thought centres correspond to the nine major endocrine glands in the physical body. The vibrating and twisting thought strings existing between the nine glands are formative of the elementary particles and the actual matter of the physical form.

Figure 2 shows the two equilateral triangles fused over the central point marked 0. The triangles have opposite spin, providing polarity to each manifestation of the numbers which physically create the energy or thought centre of the life support glands of the body.

Figure 3 is an adjusted and expanded version of the previous diagram, with the numbers for those energy or thought centres related to the spinal column and glandular functions positioned vertically. It also illustrates the input of free energetic thought

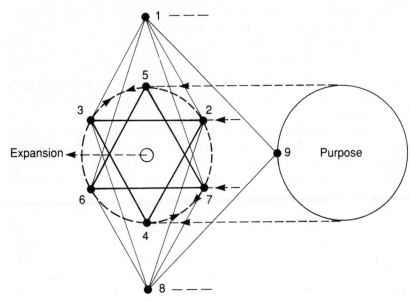

Figure 2   The fusion of matter and antimatter symbolically represented as triangles of clockwise and anti-clockwise energy

at conception of the foetus into 9 and the expansion through 0 (zero) for the production of the next cell in the metabolic process – or, macrocosmically speaking, the next dimension. An important feature to note are the ten centres of thought (0–9) and the twenty-two meridians or thought strings linking them. The combination of these two numbers gives us thirty-two. This metaphysical explanation of the fusion between matter and antimatter concurs with the first principles of the ten symbols of the Qabalistic *Tree of Life*, the twenty-two pathways of expanding consciousness, and also functions as a personification of numerology.

The Qabalah is a great body of theoretical and practical philosophy and psychology interwoven into the religious texts of the Jews, and is a vast complex of alchemical and astrological knowledge. The Hebrew word Qabalah means both to 'receive' and to 'reveal'. The diagram used in the Qabalah is known as the Tree of Life; its ten spheres and twenty-two pathways can be used as a 'map' to show the stages and levels of our consciousness. Fully understood, the Qabalah offers a unique system of personal exploration and development, allowing us to

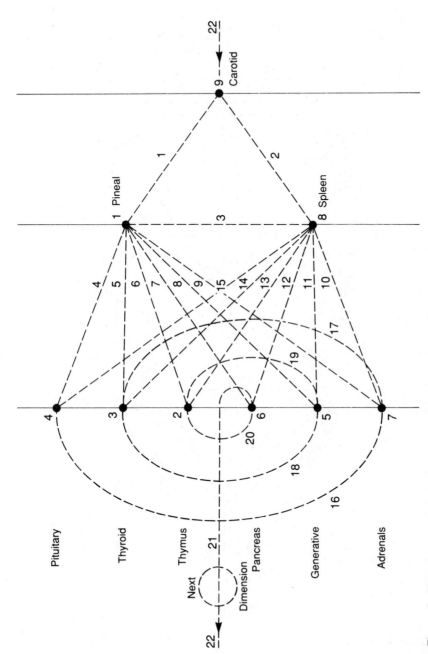

Figure 3 Energy centres of the human physical form

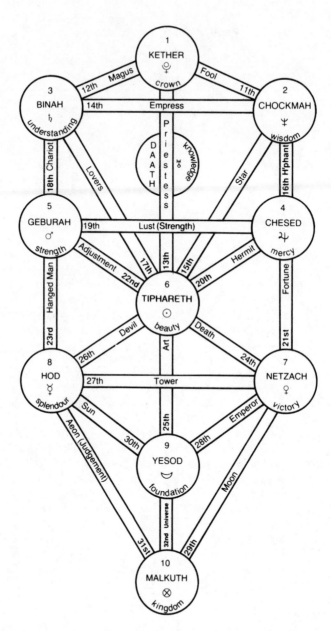

Figure 4   The Tree of Life

examine all aspects of ourselves – our personality, soul and spirit.

The *I Ching*, the Chinese *Book of Changes*, is widely regarded as a basic guide for the interpretation of living consciousness, demonstrating the link between spiritual and physical life. In the *I Ching* we encounter the magic number sixty-four in the sixty-four hexagrams, or six-line signs, each of which represents a specific configuration of relationships. The first two hexagrams represent the polar opposites of Heaven (Heaven Below, Heaven Above) and Earth (Earth Below, Earth Above). The detail here shows the positive and negative – day/night, light/dark, sun/moon, etc. The positive and negative polarities of the ten energy centres and the twenty-two pathways, depicted in Figure 3, also provide us with sixty-four dimensions or thought forms.

The symbolic proposal contained in Figure 3 enables us to view elements of metaphysical knowledge and modern biology simultaneously, making comparisons and links between the two. For example, the numerical values from the ancient traditions mentioned above can be related to the mind element of cells that exists between the fusion of the pronuclei and the thirty-two cell stage. The pattern illustrated in Figure 3 is a symbolic representation of the structure that must exist in each cell as cleavage occurs. When implantation occurs the blueprint illustrated in Figure 3 is set, determining the strengths and weaknesses of each centre and its related pathways and thus providing the ground base or thought form for the developing organism.

The nine energy centres numbered 1–9 in Figure 3 appear to control the development of the physical glands in the body which are necessary for the support of total life within the organism. These nine centres have a physical (matter) and a conscious (antimatter) function, and exist not only for the endergonic process of free energy exchange in individual cells but also exist as electromagnetic energy fields around the human form.

I believe that this total blueprint of information for purpose and structure exists within the very mitochondria of the cell. In accordance with the wave-particle duality of quantum theory, the blueprint also exists as both a wave form and a particle.

The theory of the sixty-four thought forms mentioned above

goes some way towards providing an explanation of how each cell has a mind of its own and, at the same time, an awareness of the whole organism. For the organism to become a human form its total intelligence must consist of a mind component from the consciousness of antimatter, and another from the elements that form matter.

As mentioned earlier, the mind element of matter manifests itself in the repair and reproduction of cells, both in and out of the body. The mind element of antimatter establishes the order from the universal mind. The third dimension is the identity of the individual (that is, 'you' or 'I') which chooses a point in time and space to fuse matter and antimatter together in the creation of a human organism. The dimensions of purpose, mind and matter are established at the moment of conception, and the foetus can now develop towards its first breath.

A challenging question for both science and medicine is where does humanity stand in relation to the universe? There appear to be two ways of answering this question. First, the familiar scientific/medical explanation that human beings are creatures with limitations – with minds confined to the brains of our bodies, and locked into the present time. When life runs out our bodies perish, and us with them. The second option is to consider the life force as emanating from a living world of antimatter to construct a human form which, when its purpose is fulfilled, returns to the living world of antimatter, enriched from the lessons it has learned.

Certain aspects of religious thought have long proposed the latter model – that is, life as being unbounded by space and time, with physical matter (the body) as the vehicle for the expression of the soul. Whether or not we can readily assimilate concepts such as *soul* or *spirit*, the time must surely be approaching for a dialogue between the science of medicine (including physics) and the science of metaphysics. There are too many similarities of natural phenomena becoming apparent, at both local and non-local levels, for such a dialogue to remain unconsidered for very long. A similar dialogue is also essential between those who practise scientific medicine and the practitioners of complementary medicine who draw on the many traditional methods, including those of the East.

CHAPTER 2

The First Breath

The purpose and blueprint of life embodied in each individual is established between the moment of conception and the drawing of the first breath. This is the period during which hereditary physical and mental characteristics are received from both parents, and the strengths and weaknesses of the individual's physical constitution, as well as his or her predominant mental and emotional temperament, attitudes and desires, are determined. During this time the biochemic make-up of the unborn individual is also established, as are, at another more subtle level, the influences of various universal energies and cosmological forces.

These diverse elements come together in the constitution of an individual, and their tangible expression in terms of a practical and workable formula provides us with a useful framework as a point of reference in the treatment of patients. For example, when a comparison is made between the patient's symptoms and the patient's essential blueprint or constitutional formula, the resulting information should lead us towards the underlying cause of the illness or disease. It can also be helpful to consult the patient's chart, drawn up at the consultation, in conjunction with those of his or her parents, bearing in mind that the female egg and male sperm from which the patient evolves also contain their own individual blueprints.

Before translating the blueprint into a formula which can be represented through a series of practical charts and diagrams, it is worth briefly recalling the main propositions contained in the preceding chapter.

First, there is the increasing correlation between physical, biological and metaphysical theories. Taken individually, each of these provides us with an understanding of the human organism from one specialized viewpoint. When these different viewpoints are combined they each provide a unique contribution towards a more holistic and unified understanding.

Second, the influence of what is referred to as the 'mind element'. In the developing foetus the mind element of matter present within each cell of the foetus influences the development of the individual cell and the production and development of further cells within the foetus as a whole. The mind element of antimatter influences the development of the energy centres governing purpose, attitudes and desires. It is these energy centres, or points of endergonic exchange, and their influence on the physical form that produce the individuality within human-kind.

Third, the fusion of matter and antimatter at conception, which brings into being 'you' and 'I', is caused by what we may regard as a third dimension or factor. This third dimension, the causal factor which provides each individual with his or her own unique identity, is the dimension of *purpose*.

BIOCHEMISTRY

We know that the human body is made up of billions of cells, each one of which is a complete living unit that not only forms the body tissues but is also self-reproducing. The composition of each cell varies according to its particular function within the body – for example, blood or bone cells are different from the cells of skin or nerve tissue. The material from which the cells are built obviously plays an important role in maintaining the health of the different types of body tissues and fluids. This material is derived from the food we eat and drink, and can be divided into three categories: water, organic and inorganic substances. (The importance of following a balanced diet containing the necessary nutrients should be obvious, especially during ill-health, and we shall be examining the role of the patient's diet in a later chapter.) The organic materials are protein, carbohydrate and fat. The inorganic materials are the chemical elements or minerals (iron, calcium, sodium, etc.). It is these chemical elements which form the basis of the biochemic system of medicine.

The term 'biochemistry' is derived from *bios*, Greek for 'the course of life', and 'chemistry', the study of substances, and their composition and behaviour. We might also call it the chemistry of living matter, or the chemistry of life itself.

The biochemic strengths and weaknesses of the unborn individual are determined during the period between conception and birth. It is therefore important to take into account the maternal influence when assessing the biochemistry of cells and cell metabolism. As the mother provides the environment for the developing foetus once implantation has taken place at the thirty-two cell stage, so the environment she herself experiences will in turn have some effect on the foetus, especially during the final or confinement period of pregnancy.

We have already suggested that matter cannot, of itself, produce the form of the human foetus. It is here that we once again encounter purpose, the causal factor that manifests as the mind element in matter. Perhaps we could even say that this element, present in both organic and inorganic matter, governs the biochemistry of the human body.

BIOCHEMISTRY AND COSMOLOGY

Biochemistry has its scientific origins in distant history but its more recent formulation as a system of medicine was effected by Dr Wilhelm Schuessler in the nineteenth century. The system devised by Schuessler recognized the role played by twelve principal minerals (commonly referred to as 'cell' or 'tissue' salts) in sustaining the healthy chemistry of the human body. A deficiency of one or more of these salts produces an imbalance in body chemistry, resulting in disease or illness. Of course, there are actually many more than these twelve mineral salts present in the human body – the medieval alchemists, expressing man's relationship with the universe through the concept of *microcosm* (man, the 'little world') and *macrocosm* (the universe or 'great world'), believed that the human body contained traces of *all* the elements (mineral and other) present in the universe. An extension of this perception of man's integrated relationship with the cosmos regards the functioning of the principal organs (liver, spleen, etc.) of the human body as being governed by the major planets.

For many people, the common perception of astrology as being little more than a vehicle for personal 'fortune-telling' has led to it being dismissed as a 'pseudo-science'. The primary concern of astrologers, however, is the everchanging configuration of the major planets and the corresponding variations in cosmic influence this exerts upon the earth (and its inhabitants).

The effect of this influence and its relation to displacements in planetary position is perhaps most readily accepted when it occurs in the form of an observable physical phenomenon; for example, the rise and fall of tides – a phenomenon which corresponds to the changing position of the moon in relation to the earth, increasing in strength during the new and full moons when the influence of the sun itself is also more in evidence. The effects of this influence on human behaviour are acknowledged too in our use of the word 'lunatic' (from the Latin *luna*, the moon). It is therefore possible to ascertain, as certain biochemic practitioners have done, that planetary position can be of profound importance when considering the biochemistry of the human form. For this reason the twelve principal cell or tissue salts have been linked to the twelve astrological signs.

In simple terms, each astrological 'sign' or 'house' corresponds to a particular phase of the earth's orbit and is governed by the position of the earth in relation to the sun; hence the term 'sun sign'. For example, in the northern hemisphere the Spring or Vernal Equinox (when days and nights are of equal length) occurs on March 21st, and the Summer Solstice (the longest day and shortest night) on June 21st. The position of the earth in relation to the sun in these instances corresponds to the sun entering respectively the astrological signs of Aries (the beginning of the astrological year and the first sign of the zodiac) and Cancer. As the sun exerts its cosmic influence on the planet as a whole, the astrological signs apply to both northern and southern hemispheres.

Although we may recognize the function of certain biochemical mineral or cell salts (for example, sodium for maintaining the balance in body fluids; potassium for growth; calcium for bone structure and fertility, etc.) how do we know that biochemistry is affected by planetary influence?

From experience gained in my own practice I have found

that there is a distinct correlation between the strengths and weaknesses in patients' biochemistry and the dominant planetary influence at the time of their conception and birth. In this way, simply by knowing a particular patient's astrological sign, I have been able to describe to him or her the physical symptoms from which they are suffering. Such a procedure rarely fails, but there is nothing magical or mysterious involved. All that concerns the practitioner is establishing the dominant planetary or astrological configuration at these times. The influence this exerts on the biochemistry of the foetus will be revealed more fully as the individual develops in later life, not only in their biochemic make-up but also in their body type and characteristics.

Most people interested in matters of health have asked themselves at one time or another how it is that some people manage to maintain a seemingly robust state of health in spite of what may be regarded as an unhealthy or even self-abusive life style. In direct contrast, there are those who are scrupulously careful about their health and diet, and yet suffer endlessly from this or that ailment or illness, perhaps even developing one or more chronic conditions during the course of their life. A similar predicament exists regarding the form or characteristics of the physical body. There are some people who, conscious of their tendency to put on weight, will rigorously follow this or that diet in their endeavours to retain a slim figure. Nevertheless, whatever diet they follow, they will put weight back on almost faster than they can lose it. At the other extreme, there are those who appear to consume much greater quantities of food and yet maintain an even body weight throughout their lives.

How can we relate a patient's predisposition towards certain illnesses or physical characteristics to his or her astrological sign? One possible explanation of this relationship is the tendency for the individual to experience a deficiency in the cell salt associated with their birth or sun sign. This is because, in the normal day-to-day conditions of life, we each use up more of our birth salt than any other. A deficiency in a particular cell salt produces a weakness at a biochemical level, resulting in the patient developing certain symptoms. To give a few examples: Sagittarians may be susceptible to chest conditions; Taureans to throat and respiratory troubles; Virgos to intestinal or digestive complaints; Capricorns to calcium deficiencies, rheumatism or kidney complaints, and so on. It is important, however, to remember that these are *potential* weaknesses only – because a person is born under a certain astrological sign, it does not mean that they are morally bound to develop these weaknesses! Astrological influence may also have a bearing on an individual's choice of career, their tastes in music and art, or their attitude of mind towards events on a personal or global scale – but we shall go into this in more detail in the later chapters that describe the make-up of the various blueprints.

Before we begin to develop this information into chart form, it is perhaps worth saying that the influences outlined above provide us with only one or two aspects of the total blueprint of an individual. Determining the cause of illness or disease in a patient according to a combination of biochemic and astrological theory is a significant step forward which may provide us with a satisfactory remedy or solution, but it does not yet provide us with a complete picture of the patient's blueprint and purpose.

In order to create a diagram that will provide us with a method for collating the biochemic and astrological information for each individual, we need to represent the development of the foetus in diagrammatic form. For this, it is important not only to know the date of birth but also to establish the point of conception. This may not always be known but can easily be established by working backwards to a date nine months or 280 days before birth – assuming of course that the pregnancy runs to full term. Initially the foetus develops slowly, taking a few days for the process of cleavage to arrive at the thirty-two cell stage. Gradually the rate of growth accelerates, with the major period of growth occurring between the third and sixth months. At six months, the foetus is fully formed and the growth rate then decelerates during the final three months of pregnancy.

In Figure 5 we have superimposed the points of conception and birth, and the three- and six-month points indicating the period of sustained growth, on a circle divided into twelve segments. The rate of growth of the foetus is indicated by the tadpole-like shape which resembles the foetal form and simultaneously divides the circle into two, giving us an image that resembles the ancient *Yin-Yang* symbol of Chinese medicine. These two divisions are distinguished as 'positive' and 'negative'. The area of the diagram between the points of birth and conception is what I call the *quadrant of purpose* and it

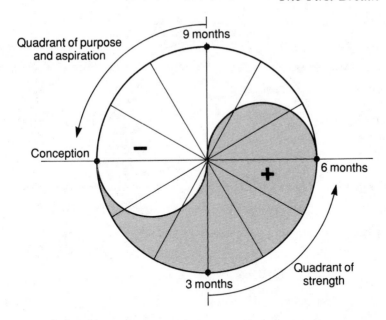

Figure 5 The development of the foetus: points of conception and birth

will be noted that this lies opposite the quadrant of strength or sustained growth marked by the three- and six-month points.

When the relevant information for the individual patient is superimposed on Figure 5, it is important to consider the percentages of the segments covered by the diagrammatic development of the foetus, as these indicate the attributes of character and biochemistry which will manifest themselves in later life. In a similar way the individual's predisposition to certain weaknesses and desires is portrayed by the negative or 'purpose' side of the symbol.

The next stage is to extend the information in our diagram in relation to the point of conception by indicating the twelve astrological signs and, for each sign, its known biochemic mineral salt, and a numerical symbol that refers to the energy centre and glandular function associated with it, as confirmed during my research and practice. This we do in Figure 6 which illustrates how the information would appear for someone conceived under the astrological sign of Libra. Our diagram now shows us the predominant signs, dates, and tissue salt pertaining to a particular individual.

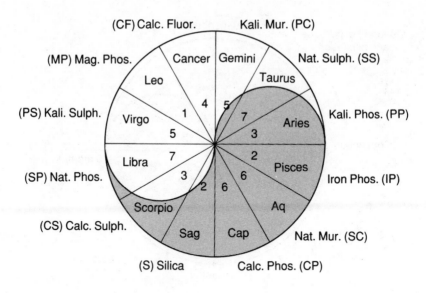

Figure 6 The development of the foetus: biochemistry and astrology

It will be noted that the direction of movement for the astrological signs in the diagram is anticlockwise. Some readers may question this layout of the zodiac but my own experience has shown me that this anticlockwise movement portrays convincingly, for our current purpose, the effects imparted on the earth by cosmic influence.

The influence of biochemistry on the development of the cell structures in the foetus is clearly depicted in Figure 6. A further consideration is the parallel development of the tangible thought forms of attitudes, desires, virtues and vices (illustrated in Figure 1 on page 22). These are indicated by the numerical values I have ascribed to each astrological sign – for example, Aries 3, Taurus 7, and so on. This additional dimension attributes Aries with the thought forms of higher active intelligence and Taurus those of physical willpower. We can detail this information as follows:

Scorpio, Aries	3	Higher active intelligence
Libra, Taurus	7	Physical will and excretion
Virgo, Gemini	5	Intellect and procreation
Cancer	4	Harmony from conflict

Leo	1	Spiritual purpose and will
Pisces, Sagittarius	2	Love and wisdom
Capricorn, Aquarius	6	Devotion and digestion

Categories 8 and 9, which were mentioned earlier and appear in Figure 3, are not included in the astrological or confinement chart (Figures 5 and 6). They relate directly to emotion and mentality which are both acquired and inherited characteristics. However, when interpreting the total blueprint, Figures 3 and 6 are used simultaneously.

THE BLUEPRINT FORMULA

As the foetus grows and develops towards its first breath, so the total individual blueprint for life is formed. At the chosen moment when the first breath is taken a profound pattern is set. There can be no change, no going back. The life purpose for the individual is fixed, and his or her constitution, biochemic strengths and weaknesses, and tangible thought forms and attitudes are all known factors.

How can these factors be known with any certainty? This is the function of the *blueprint formula*. The formula is based on ten components of irreversible fact, unique to the life of each individual. By completing the formula with details of static information pertaining to an individual, we arrive at a series of numerical values which form the blueprint for that individual. As we shall see from the components listed below, the chances of more than one person having the same series of numbers appearing in an identical order are millions to one.

The ten components of the Blueprint Formula are:

A Numerical value of day of birth
B Numerical value of zodiac category
C Numerical value of year of birth
D Numerical value of total day, month and year
E Numerical value of essence of country of birth
F Numerical value of personality of country of birth
G Numerical value of essence of family name
H Numerical value of personality of family name
I Numerical value of essence of given name
J Numerical value of personality of given name

Before giving a detailed example of the blueprint at work, the following explanations outline the method for obtaining the different numerical values. Note that, where necessary, the numerical value for each component is reduced to a single digit by a series of additions.

A   The numerical value attributed to the day of birth for a person born on the 9th would be 9. For a person born on the 10th it would be 1 (1+0=1); the 24th, 6 (2+4=6); the 29th, 2 (2+9=11, 1+1=2), and so on. This system of addition applies to all components.

B   For the zodiac category, take the number that corresponds to the relevant astrological sign in Figure 6. For example, for those persons born between November 22nd and December 21st (Sagittarius), we would enter 2 for this numerical value; for Taureans, born between April 21st and May 22nd, a 7, etc.

C   To obtain the numerical value for the year of birth, add together the four digits to arrive at a single number. For a person born in 1965, this value would be 3 (1+9+6+5=21, 2+1=3).

D   The total day, month and year is calculated in a similar way. For a person born 10.12.1965, we would enter the numerical value of 7 (1+0+1+2+1+9+6+5=25, 2+5=7).

E   For the values attributed to the essence (E) and personality (F) of the country of birth, and an explanation of these values, consult Chart 1 (see page 40). For a person born in South Africa, the value for E is 2.

F   For a person born in South Africa, the value to enter for the personality is 4.

G   The numerical values for the essence (G) and personality (H) of the family name are arrived at simultaneously by a method of calculation for which the letters of the alphabet are first translated into numerical values (see Chart 2 p. 42). For a married woman, her own maiden or family name is used, *not* her married family name. The method of calculating these numerical values using the family name MASON as an example is as follows:

Divide the vowels from the consonants

$$\frac{\text{A} \quad \text{O}}{\text{M} \quad \text{S} \quad \text{N}}$$

This produces an equation of sound, as both vowels and consonants represent speech sounds which can be expressed numerically, by exchanging the letters for numbers.

$$\frac{\text{A} \quad \text{O}}{\text{M} \quad \text{S} \quad \text{N}} \text{ becomes } \frac{1 + 7}{4 + 3 + 5} = \frac{8}{12} = \frac{8}{1 + 2} = \frac{8}{3}$$

The total for the vowels (upper line) gives us the numerical
value for G, the essence of the family name, which in this case
is 8.

H The numerical value for the personality of the family name
is the total for the consonants (lower line). The number we
would enter for MASON would be 3.

I The same process applies to the essence (I) and personality
(J) of the given name (that is, the Christian or first name).
Using the name RICHARD as an example, the calculation is as
follows:

Divide the vowels from the consonants

$$\frac{\text{I} \quad \text{A}}{\text{R} \quad \text{CH} \quad \text{R D}}$$

which numerically equals:

$$\frac{1 + 1}{2 + 8 + 2 + 4} = \frac{2}{16} = \frac{2}{1 + 6} = \frac{2}{7}$$

(Note that CH = 8; see Chart 2.)
   The numerical value for the essence of the name RICHARD
would be entered as 2.

J The personality of the name RICHARD is calculated as 7.
So, for Richard Mason born 10.12.1965 in South Africa, the
result is as follows:

A Numerical value of day of birth – 10th   1
B Numerical value of zodiac category – Sagittarius   2
C Numerical value of year of birth – 1965   3
D Numerical value of total day, month, year – 10.12.1965   7
E Numerical value of essence of country – South Africa   2
F Numerical value of personality of country – South Africa   4

G   Numerical value of essence of family name – Mason   8
H   Numerical value of personality of family name – Mason   3
I   Numerical value of essence of given name – Richard   2
J   Numerical value of personality of given name – Richard   7

The total blueprint for Richard Mason consists of the following numbers in their given order. Set at his first breath, they represent his blueprint for life:

1. 2. 3. 7. 2. 4. 8. 3. 2. 7.

CHART 1

The following chart gives the numerical values of both the essence and personality of the listed countries (components E and F). The list includes only those countries where patients have been treated, and for which the values have been calculated and found correct during many years of research working directly with patients suffering from chronic illness.

The populations in all countries of the world display distinctive national tendencies and characteristics. There are also national attitudes which can be described as a nation's *essence* and *personality*.

The true *essence* of a nation can also be referred to as its heart, mind or spirit. It reveals itself in the way in which the individuals within a nation appear to be joined in their actions and responses by a common thread of consciousness. Perhaps we could also describe the essence of a country as its soul, or group consciousness. The *personality* of a country differs from this group consciousness in that it is more the public face of a nation – the conscious national identity or particularism subscribed to collectively by the individuals that together make up the population of a country. In other words, it is the image a nation projects of itself through its particularisms and characteristics of exclusiveness – its chosen views, reactions, and systems of class or caste and individualism – with regard to a current environment. To sum up these two qualities: essence is *karmic*, deeprooted and latent, whereas personality is changeable within certain boundaries of the national identity.

Country	Essence	Personalilty	Country	Essence	Personalilty
Argentine	4	2	Italy	6	3
Australia	5	3	Japan	2	5
Austria	4	5	Kenya	6	5
Belgium	3	4	Mexico	3	4
Brazil	4	2	Nigeria	7	6
Canada	2	3	Pakistan	1	4
China	1	3	Poland	2	7
Finland	2	7	Romania	7	2
France	5	3	Russia	7	6
Germany	4	1	Scandinavia		
Great Britain	2	1	(4 nations)	5	7
Greece	6	4	South Africa	2	4
Holland	4	5	Spain	6	7
India	1	4	Switzerland	7	4
Ireland (Rep.)	7	5	Turkey	2	4
Israel	7	3	USA	2	6

Although people may move from one country to another and
even spend most of their life in a different country from that
of their birth, their essence or blueprint retains the consciousness of their country of origin. And in this respect it should be
noted that it is the country of birth that is dominant, not the
country of conception. People who emigrate to a new country
may feel that they are affected by the characteristics of their
adoptive nation, but the effect is localized at the level of their
personality and does not affect their vital essence.

CHART 2

'In the beginning was the Word. . . . and the Word was made
flesh.' The 'word' is sound, and sound, as vibration, is a measurable wave form. Wave-particle duality means that a wave form
can also be a particle, and so sound can become form. It is
therefore possible to create a bipolar form from a word,
enabling a name to take on form or matter.

To create the resonance of form from sound, we turn the
family or given name into an equation by replacing letters with
numbers. One of the oldest traditional letter-codes is based on
the sounds that occur in the Hebrew alphabet. Chart 2 shows
the twenty-two Hebrew letters with their English equivalents
and the numerical value attributed to that sound.

Number	Hebrew letter	English letter, or consonant sounds	Numerical value
1	Aleph	A	1
2	Beth	B	2
3	Gimel	G (NB: *not* C)	3
4	Daleth	D	4
5	He	E	5
6	Vau	V, U, W	6
7	Zain	Z	7
8	Cheth	H, CH	8
9	Teth	TH	9
10	Jod	I, Y, J	1
11	Caph	C, K	2
12	Lamed	L	3
13	Mem	M	4
14	Nun	N	5
15	Samek	X	6
16	Ayin	O	7
17	Peh	F, P, PH	8
18	Tzaddi	SH, TS, TZ	9
19	Quoph	Q	1
20	Resh	R	2
21	Shin	S	3
22	Tau	T	4

As the numerical value corresponding to each letter represents a subtle force or energy, the equation derived from each family name using Chart 2 provides us with an interesting insight; in understanding how families in similar environments within a community will manifest different reactions and patterns of behaviour.

We must now turn our attention to interpreting the numerical values of the blueprint, as an understanding of the deeper meaning expressed by the numbers will provide us with a complete picture of the developing child.

The glands of the body are created and governed during life by the wave form or energy fields emanating from certain energy field centres existing around the body. Each centre plays an active part in supporting the life of the individual, but certain glands and centres will be more active than others. Those centres found to be missing a percentage numerical value will be the areas for purpose or aspiration (see Figure 7).

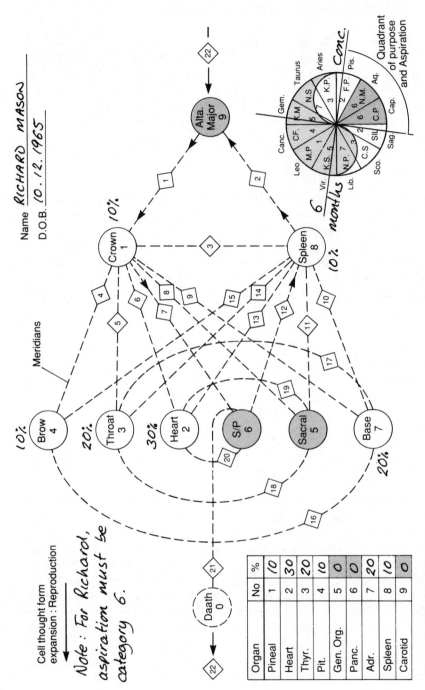

Figure 7 The blueprint

Before explaining more fully in the next chapter the method of interpretation (with examples), we must first show the glands and energy centres with their unchanging identity. Figure 7 has unfolded from the original Figures 1 and 2, and is to be compared with the astrological influence illustrated in Figure 6.

The percentages shown against the numbered energy centres are obtained by the following method. In our example, we use the total numerical blueprint for Richard Mason which is:

1. 2. 3. 7. 2. 4. 8. 3. 2. 7.

Let us examine the possible percentages of the numerical values with reference to the nine energy centres. Working in numerical order, we proceed like this: How many times does the number 1 occur in the sequence of ten blueprint numbers? Once, so that gives us 1 in 10, or 10 per cent. How many 2s are there? Three, giving us 30 per cent. So taking the blueprint as a total (100 per cent) of a person's vibration, it would read like this:

Gland	No.	%	
Pineal	1	10	average
Thymus	2	30	strength of character (strongest)
Thyroid	3	20	strong
Pituitary	4	10	average
Gonads	5	nil	aspiration?
Pancreas	6	nil	aspiration?
Adrenals	7	20	strong
Spleen	8	10	average
Carotid	9	nil	aspiration?
Total		100%	

As shown above, the percentages indicate varying strengths of character. Taking 10 per cent as an average, 20 per cent indicates a strong disposition while 30 per cent or more reveals a marked strength of character. A person's blueprint will often indicate at least one pronounced strength of character, or, alternatively, more general areas of strength. There will, however, always be an area with a nil percentage. Biochemically speaking, these are the areas of possible weakness in the physical body but, more importantly, they are areas of aspiration; that is, they are the areas of cause or purpose of the individual, and he or she aspires to develop the consciousness relevant to the corresponding numerical values.

Perhaps another way of looking at this is to say that the vital essence of an individual manifests itself as a form of matter via the physical body. When considered from this point of view, we can go on to state that the blueprint, with its characteristics of physical and conscious strengths and aspirations, provides us with a tangible framework that reveals the aspiration and purpose for the life of an individual.

CHART 3

Chart 3 shows the numerical values and their related energy centres. The site of each centre is given, along with the gland through which energy from the centre passes into the physical body, and the particular area of the body these govern.

No.	Centre	Situation	Physical gland	Area governed
1	Crown	A vortex above top of head but which surrounds physical body as a field	Pineal	Right creative brain; right eye; right side of head; desire and emotion
4	Brow	Between eyes	Pituitary	Left brain; left eye; ears; nose; sinuses; nervous system
3	Throat	The neck	Thyroid	Bronchial; vocal; lungs; alimentary canal
2	Heart	Between shoulder blades; sternum	Thymus	Heart; blood immune system; vagus nerve; circulation
6	Solar plexus	Above waist	Pancreas	Stomach; liver; gall bladder; nervous system
5	Sacral	Below waist	Gonads	Reproductive system
7	Base	Apex of sacrum	Adrenal	Spinal column; kidneys; willpower; locomotion
8	Spleen	Left of navel and above waist but as a field around the body	Spleen	Blood; skin
9	Alta Major	Base of occiput, but also as a field outside emotional fields of 1 to 8	Carotid plexus	Spine; blood pressure; fluids

ENERGY CENTRES GOVERNING GLANDS AND ORGAN SYSTEMS

The information in the above chart begins to give an idea of the power of the numerical system by indicating some of the energies and forces associated with each of the nine numbers. To take this a stage further, the following categories outline the various characteristics, attitudes of mind, and vices and virtues I have found to correspond to the different numerical values.

The reader will note that each energy centre (which I also refer to as a thought centre or as a category) contains two principal aspects, referred to as positive and negative. A similar bipolarity necessarily occurs at all levels of life's activity, whether this manifests as positive and negative at the level of thought form, or physical matter, or as the virtues and vices that make up the character of an individual's personality. Singular polarity is not creative and so life should be the recognition of both dimensions with one's actions stemming naturally and positively from the apparent duality of events. The negative aspects or vices of each category will only manifest when they are the course of action chosen (consciously or unconsciously) by the individual.

It is worth mentioning at this stage that when a person acts against a strength of character indicated by one of the nine categories of their blueprint, perhaps by taking the easy way out and opting for the negative attitude, a polarization of wave form will occur in the area of the body governed by that category. A poor or inaccurate wave form function of this kind will manifest as particle interference in the cell metabolism – in other words, disease of the physical form. In later chapters we will examine in greater detail how the thought forms and wave vibrations emanating from the individual's energy fields can cause a malfunctioning in the matter that forms the physical body.

Category 1: Will and Power

Energy centre   Crown
Associated gland   Pineal
Area governed   Right hemisphere of brain (the intuitive and

creative mind); right eye; right side of head. This centre also governs the desires and emotions.

Summary *Positive* Very strong character. Naturally intuitive and creative, with the will and ability to put ideas into action. Adaptability; self-confidence; diplomacy in dealing with others. *Negative* Obstinacy; timidity; manipulation of others.

Positive aspects or virtues The combination of will and power leads to great strength of character. Those with a strong percentage in this category are naturally intuitive people; the link between intuition and will is such that they not only intuitively *know* when something is right, they also have the mental and physical resolve to act in response to this intuitive knowledge. The ability to act intuitively leads to a lack of fear when faced with problems in business or personal life.

These are the people who generate new ideas, for intuition, initiative and creativity go hand in hand. They have a breadth of vision which enables them to understand the many aspects of the wider issues of life. This makes them adaptable and versatile, providing them with skilful powers of arbitration and a diplomatic ability to organize people in both business and the wider community. Strength of initiative and self-confidence means that they are always involved at the beginnings of new cycles of life or business developments. These same qualities lead to success in business, and in their business dealings they are very fair and honest. They may sometimes be calculating, but not in a dishonest way. In their contacts with people they are steadfast and truthful. They are able to influence the events around them by manifesting the thought forms of others, purely through the strength of their mind power.

Category 1 inclines us to strive to unravel the very meaning of life itself. This may often be pursued against great odds, but intuition and true creative imagination are there to help us reach our goal. It is important to recognize our own capabilities and strengths, allowing them to flow through our essence and so build the purpose of our life. This expansion of the personality, from the inside outwards, which is characteristic of this category, is the same creative drive that provides us with great and beautiful art.

Negative aspects or vices The positive strength of character from Category 1 manifests itself negatively as timidity, weakness of will, and a lack of resolve. These attitudes bring further problems with them and may even result in an inability to face the reality of life. Alternatively, the virtues of Category 1 can become vices, turning into obstinacy and pride, with an over-strong ambition leading to the desire to control others to their detriment.

Aspirational aspects   Tenderness and humility. The development of a sympathetic attitude towards others, governed by patience and tolerance, especially with those less able than one-self.

Possible physical weaknesses   Failures in the nervous system.

From the above information the reader will begin to understand that those individuals with a large percentage of Category 1 in their blueprint have the potential to use all the attributes and characteristics mentioned. It will also be seen how those with a *nil* reading for this category should aspire to attain these qualities during their lifetimes, fulfilling their purpose by the acquisition of these positive aspects or virtues.

When a patient shows signs of illness related to the areas governed by a particular category, he or she will also display a corresponding excess at a mental level in either the positive or negative aspects associated with that category. For example, in Category 1, excessive ambition and the will to manipulate others to suit one's own wishes or needs could create abnormal emotional desires, leading to physical illness: right-sided headaches, neuralgia, nerve depletion within the brain, and perhaps even Parkinson's disease.

Category 2: Love and Wisdom

Energy centre   Heart
Associated gland   Thymus
Area governed   Heart; blood immune system; vagus nerve; circulation.
Summary   *Positive*   Love extends to all humanity. Calmness; patience and understanding; faithfulness; strength and courage. Intuitive insight and right timing of action. *Negative*   Coldness and indifference to others; selfishness. Fear, and an accompanying loss or waste of opportunities.
Positive aspects or virtues   The word 'love' means many things

to many people because love manifests itself in many guises. Our own historical time is marked by a tendency both to emotional display and emotional disorder. That is why love and wisdom are joined together in this category, for love is much more than just an emotion or a physical attraction to another person. Wisdom enables one to learn through love, and learning how to give and receive love is one way to attain wisdom.

As a result of this, people with a strong percentage in Category 2 display many of the high ideals associated with the noble knights of medieval legend, whose exploits were motivated by an apparently virtuous love. They possess the calmness and strength which are synonymous with courage. In their relationships with others they are faithful, patient and understanding, and their love for humanity as a whole makes them people of truth and integrity. Their intuition gives them insights into the problems or situations that confront them, and their clear intellect enables them to act in the right way at the right time. Artists and innovators have a strong resonance from Category 2 as this category provides the knowledge and know-how needed to implement new ideas and innovations.

Negative aspects or vices The polar opposite of love is coldness and indifference to others and this is the principal negative aspect of Category 2. This negative pole or vice may also arise, however, from over-absorption in study or other intellectual activity. In the latter case, this may be accompanied by a particular indifference to, perhaps even contempt for, those of a lower mental ability – a clear reversal of both love and wisdom.

There is a tendency for the artists, innovators, and others who resonate to this category to lack patience and be dissatisfied with their highest attainments as their minds are always searching for something new. Courage in the negative becomes fear. Fear, whether arising from known or unknown causes, can develop into inferiority complexes, feelings of inadequacy, and self-pity. Fear can also manifest as losing one's nerve, leading to lost opportunities. Couple this with a lack of foresight and one is forever wasting the opportunities that present themselves because they always seem to occur at the wrong time and in the wrong place.

Aspirational aspects Extend love to humanity, developing calmness and patience in dealing with others. Learn to use intuition and to be creative. Work to overcome fear.

Possible physical weaknesses Category 2 is related to the thymus gland and immune deficiency illnesses. A breakdown in the immune system is a sign that the matter that makes up the physical body is losing, or has lost, the ability to create form. As the creation of form is a bipolar activity, requiring both a positive and a negative, the necessity of bipolarity for the successful attainment of purpose in nature should not be ignored. A conscious bipolar attitude of love and wisdom, developed by adhering to the positive attitudes of Category 2 and its possibilities of purpose, often brings renewed health from apparently otherwise incurable illness.

Category 3: Higher Active Intelligence

Energy centre Throat
Associated gland Thyroid
Area governed Vocal; bronchial; lungs; alimentary canal
Summary *Positive* Concern for the spiritual and philosophical issues in life. Clear intellect, with flexible, sympathetic outlook. *Negative* Materialism; intellectual pride; finicky attention to detail; inflexibility.
Positive aspects or virtues Flexibility of mind means that people of this category have the ability to adapt to changing circumstances. They will listen to the guidance and wisdom of others, as well as listening to the inner self, the unconscious mind. They possess the capacity to concentrate on the more abstract and philosophical aspects of life. Their concern for 'higher things' gives them an attitude of acceptance, based on the understanding that the events of life occur for a reason and worrying about them will change nothing.

All the same, our reaction to these events needs to be the result of a clear and positive decision. When such a decision is made this category will see it through to completion without deviation or backtracking. They are patient and cautious, and their ability to wait for, and recognize, the exact moment for action brings abundance and fruitfulness into their life. Category 3 requires domestic stability. Their approach to others is sympathetic, caring for their family and friends, and offering protection to those in need.

Negative aspects of vices Category 3's interest in higher things manifests itself negatively as excessive materialism and a disregard for the spiritual dimension of life. An overprotective approach to one's family and possessions leads to selfish attitudes and criticism of others. The tendency may arise to worry about the trifling little things of life – both those affecting oneself and others. Intellectual pride or absent-mindedness may develop, along with coldness and lack of sympathy towards others, especially those of lesser understanding. When action is called for there may be a loss of nerve due to inflexibility.

Aspirational aspects A concern with the wider issues of life rather than its insignificant details, for instance, study the philosophy of life. The development of a clear intellect guided by intuition and sincerity. Adaptability, honesty and sympathy.

Possible physical weaknesses Negative attitudes of this category can lead to respiratory illnesses, asthma, emphysema, and thyroid malfunctions. As with all categories, the use of correct or positive attitudes can heal these conditions.

Category 4: Harmony out of Sacrifice or Conflict

Energy centre Brow
Associated gland Pituitary
Area governed Left brain; left eye; nose; sinuses; nervous system.
Summary *Positive* Learning from the lessons of experience. Logical left-brain thinking. Kindness and affection. *Negative* Immature and self-centred. Materialistic.
Positive aspects or virtues Conflict does not have to be violent and so perhaps the 'harmony through conflict' of Category 4 is best explained as the changes that occur in the form of blessings in disguise. Often an event – sometimes even one of an apparently unwelcome nature – clears the way forward, showing the direction of purpose after a period of conflict. The emergence from conflict, whether experienced at an inner level with oneself or at an outer level with others, coincides with the removal of out-dated or superfluous aspects of life, allowing an unhindered move forward into the future. This coincides with the fact that, for Category 4, knowledge is gained through experience, the greatest teacher of all.

There are many special virtues of this category but of particular note is the left-brain consciousness, controlling logic and discriminative thinking. These people have a quick, perceptive intellect. The strength of their affections displays itself in the kindness, sympathy, and generosity. They are lovers of colour and art and like to surround themselves with treasures and beautiful things. They also possess physical courage and a natural authority. Willpower, ambition, and self-control are further attributes of Category 4.

Negative aspects or vices Self-centredness. A lack of moral courage can fill an individual with so much worry and anxiety that when he or she attempts to overcome it they become extravagant, developing excessive passions which, in turn, can manifest as weaknesses and immaturity. There may be a lack of determination to fulfil one's own ambitions, giving way to other people instead, possibly even becoming excessively subservient to those perceived as being of a higher authority.

In the negative mode, Category 4 people are often impractical. They are changeable, switching to suit whatever may be their current environment, or from brilliant conversation to gloomy silence. Their love of fine things may lead them to place greater value on material possessions than spiritual understanding, thus ignoring the balanced polarity one should seek to attain.

Aspirational aspects Development of self-control and control of the will. The ability to learn from life's experiences. An appreciation of art and craft for their beauty, not for their material value or fashionable standing.

Possible physical weaknesses Imbalances in this category will cause illnesses related to the left hemisphere of the brain and affect the central nervous system, ears and eyes, and may result in headaches. The wave form vibrations of Category 4 manifest through the pituitary gland; because this gland plays an important role in the hormonal secretions of other endocrine glands, a lack of control and balance in Category 4 has significant consequences. Malfunction or trauma, with accompanying environmental stress in that area, is responsible for illness in many parts of the body where the pituitary function is important, particularly the ovaries and the testes, and for adrenal malfunction.

Category 5: Intellect and Procreation

Energy centre Sacral
Associated gland Gonads
Area governed Reproductive system
Summary *Positive* Strong sense of justice, accuracy and physical order. Original ideas within traditional frameworks. *Negative* Narrow-minded and uncompromising. Unsympathetic attitude towards others. Always right. Duty to impose own ideas on everybody else. Clumsy.
Positive aspects or virtues The predominant attitude here is one of 'rightness'. The personal and business affairs of people with a strength in this category are characterized by precision of statement and a strong sense of justice, with little time for those who fall foul of the law or simply muddle along with no clear goal in mind. There is an inclination to label or classify things, to record statements with accuracy, and to put items back in exactly the right place, as they like the world around them to be neat, tidy and orderly. Problems that may arise are dealt with according to known formulae.

A thirst for knowledge and the need to know the reason behind all things are matched with a keen intellect and profound thinking. Ideas proliferate from this energy centre but, in spite of their fresh and creative nature, they will always be presented within a traditional framework. Traditional knowledge is often transmitted via Category 5, especially where it combines the elucidation of profound thought with an already proven and recognized process of explanation such as mathematical theory. Those involved with the counselling professions work well when resonating to this category.
Negative aspects or vices The principal negative aspect is a narrow-minded attitude, often of an uncompromising and critical nature. There is a lack of sympathy towards others which may turn to unforgiving resentment when it is felt, rightly or wrongly, that one has been adversely affected by events. The negative of this category may also reveal itself as clumsiness, both physical and in the handling of one's own affairs and relations with other people. Such clumsiness may thwart the natural progression through life because it results in a mishandling of potentially helpful situations. In these circumstances it

is, of course, always another person or the situation itself that is seen to be at fault.

A similar intransigence is met in those individuals who, believing they have found a particular system, method or even a path in life which is right for them, are also convinced it is the right one for everybody else. They then feel it is their bounden duty to persuade others to follow the same course.

Aspirational aspects Truth and accuracy. Knowledge and science used in the service of others, not as a means to impose one's own will or ideas on them.

Possible physical weaknesses This sphere of conscious activity, especially in the seeking for knowledge, functions via the sacral centre. Imbalance or malfunction in this category may therefore result in disease of the male or female reproductive organs. If this occurs, the way to renewed health will be helped by correct thought form.

Category 6: Devotion and Digestion

Energy centre Solar plexus
Associated gland Pancreas
Area governed Stomach; liver; gall bladder; nervous system.
Summary *Positive* Devotion to others; single-mindedness; loyalty. *Negative* Selfishness, jealousy, and anger when things 'go wrong'. Indecision.
Positive aspects or virtues Devotion develops into love, tenderness, a caring for others, and loyalty and respect towards relationships and life. People with a strength in this category often follow a particular career for which they have a definite liking. They will be successful in this chosen path but in mid-life, a major event will bring about a complete change of interest and career. Although this change of heart often presents itself as the polar opposite of that previously held, it is of crucial importance for their personal development. When such a situation arises it is essential to rely on intuition, listening to the inner self or inner voice rather than being guided by intellect and reason.

Harmonious balance is essential in life. This is especially true regarding the material and spiritual dimensions where our concern with the materialistic aspects of life should not outweigh the need for spiritual understanding and belief. We should always listen to the subconscious mind or inner voice, taking care not to allow the rationalizing thought processes of the mind to repress intuitive or instinctive knowledge. The danger of such repression is that we can become too smart for our own good. We should aspire to get rid of our rigid attitudes and allow change to occur naturally, thus revealing the hidden focus of destiny working to manifest its purpose.

Negative aspects or vices   Where love is concerned, selfishness, jealousy and a fiery anger are all negative manifestations of devotion. Instead of developing the ability to make sound decisions, people often do the opposite, developing the inability to make them. They may even become suspicious of rapid decisions or conclusions. The inability to make decisions can lead to moral lapses and severe temptations, presenting them with a major challenge in another guise from which they also recoil.

Aspirational aspects   Loyalty, reverence and a willingness to take reasoned and calculated risks.

Possible physical weaknesses   As Category 6 regulates the function of the stomach, intestine and other abdominal organs, incorrect thought forms, such as selfishness and jealousy, will lead to stomach and digestive disorders.

Category 7: Physical will and excretion

Energy centre   Base
Associated gland   Adrenal
Area governed   Spinal column; kidneys; locomotion. This area also governs willpower.
Summary   *Positive*   Strength of character. Will and power, but used selflessly. *Negative*   Self-opinionated and over-indulgent; the tendency to act out of self-interest.
Positive aspects or virtues   The base of the spine and the adrenal glands – the seat of our 'fight or flight' mechanism – provide us with our strength of courage and perseverance when faced with a challenge of one kind or another. In fact, this category needs the challenge in order to respond actively to it and, in turn, the ability to respond leads us to rely on ourselves rather than on others to overcome the obstacles we encounter along

life's path. The level of material success and financial security we attain is due to our own hard work and selflessness, and is not obtained through inheritance or another similarly 'easy' way. This category also engenders a strong passion for ritual, whether it is the ritual encountered in religious, civic or other ceremonies, or the ritual found within some forms of traditional healing.

Negative aspects or vices   Self-reliance should not be confused with self-interest. Self-interest leads to excessive pride and the tendency to ride roughshod over others to get what we want, not worrying about the wider consequences of our actions. It also gives rise to a narrowness of mind, with superficial judgements and opinions which we forcefully impose on others. The temptation to be ruthless or immoral in our business dealings may occur, leading to unnecessary suffering and, eventually, our own self-undoing.

Aspirational aspects   It is important to realize that others too have their own rights and needs. Even those who adhere to beliefs and codes of behaviour that differ from our own are, in fact, progressing along their own chosen path in life, and we should learn to respect this.

Possible physical weaknesses   Kidney and bladder conditions. Adrenal exhaustion. General skeletal problems related to mobility. An impairment of the will.

Category 8: Physical purpose and desire

Energy centre   Spleen
Associated gland   Spleen
Area governed   Blood; skin.
Summary   *Positive*   Mental and emotional balance and stability predominate. Love, strength of individuality and good judgement. *Negative*   Rigidity of mind restricting personal development.
Positive aspects or virtues   People with a strength in this category are often natural but very intense, and are blessed with strong individuality. When called upon to play an important role on life's stage they benefit from sound judgement and are able to resolve the disputes of those around them through arbitration, stemming from their capacity to see both sides of

an argument. They are often great individuals whose warm hearts respond demonstratively to the oppressed people of the world. They can also hide their inner feelings, allowing others to think just what they please of them without sufferance.

The thought forms functioning through the spleen may be likened to our conscience – the inner voice to which we should always listen, and to which we owe our level of truth and integrity. This same inner voice gives us great insight into the possibilities that lie in the future, guiding us towards a fulfilling life.

Negative aspects or vices   In spite of their very deep and intense nature they may experience a loneliness of heart, feeling acutely alone even in a crowd. The inability or reluctance to broaden one's viewpoint can lead to self-doubt and a lack of trust in others. This can lead to unfair dealings in business or personal affairs, possibly resulting in legal wrangles. Similarly, a rigid mind, unable to expand beyond familiar territory, will restrict the possibility of responding to the new opportunities which form an essential part of our progress through life.

Aspirational aspects   Category 8 aspires towards harmony and balance as the spleen centre is a field of energetic activity surrounding the whole body, linking the fields of emotion and desire to mental activity. In intentionally widening his or her own physical and mental horizons, the patient will be guided towards their correct path in life.

Possible physical weaknesses   Disharmony or imbalance in the resonance of this category manifests as disease of the blood or skin.

Category 9: Purpose

Energy centre   Alta major
Associated gland   Carotid plexus
Area governed   Spine; blood pressure; body fluids.
Summary   Category 9 appears mostly as an aspiration, for we are all striving to attain perfection in this life and to experience its gifts to the full.
Positive aspects or virtues   During many years of formulating and interpreting the blueprint, I have found few people with a predominant strength in Category 9. This is hardly surprising

for most of us are aspiring towards the attainment of our goal or purpose in life. When it does occur in a blueprint, it suggests a person of very strong will and character embodying an understanding of the needs of people, animals and the world of nature. Individuals born with a resonance of 9 are great fighters in all they do. Although they may have difficulty in their earlier years, by midlife they are usually totally successful in everything to which they turn their attention.

They tend to be great planners and thinkers, never rushing headlong into things without careful consideration of the outcome and its wider effects. Generally these people are the very 'soul of discretion', going about their work peacefully and quietly without seeking applause or adulation. It is a resonance suited to counsellors and arbitrators who not only listen to others but also to the inner voice, the voice of their conscience.

Negative aspects or vices   The negative aspects are few. They can appear to be stubborn or dogmatic, creating the impression that they hold themselves aloof from their peers – an attitude that can lead to loneliness. Alternatively, they can be hasty and impulsive, with the desire to be their own masters making them visibly independent of others.

Aspirational aspects   Profound thinking. Planning, counselling, arbitration. The fullest appreciation of nature and our fellow human beings is a necessary goal, whichever path in life we choose to follow.

Possible physical weaknesses   Stress and immobility of the neck and shoulders, as Category 9 is related to the carotid nerve plexus.

THE DEVELOPING ESSENCE

At the moment of birth the blueprint, the chosen path or purpose for the life of the individual, is fixed. From this point onwards the various attitudes, characteristics and virtues that are locked into every cell and its endergonic process will never change. The only aspect of an individual that does change is his or her personality, and here it is perhaps important to define the difference between personality and purpose. The difference between the two may even be likened to that which exists between predestination and free will. The purpose of an indi-

vidual is fixed whereas the personality is variable, dealing with
the blueprint or purpose as it thinks fit. It is when the personality works against the original purpose that emotional and
mental problems arise, possibly leading to the manifestation of
illness or disease of the physical form.

The blueprint permits us to identify with certainty the underlying cause of malfunction in a patient – whether this is at an
emotional, mental or physical level – because it provides us
with a mode for the whole individual. Once the formula has
been interpreted the profile it presents is compared with the
patient's current attitudes and aspirations. At the same time
any physical symptoms are examined and the area of the body
where they occur is noted. When this information is collated,
the practitioner has a three-dimensional image of the patient –
a complete portrait of him or her at the levels of purpose, mind,
and physical form, enabling us to establish where the cause is
manifesting. The cause itself may be of an energetic or biochemic nature, and we shall return to these in future chapters.

As the child grows towards adulthood it is possible to confirm
the accuracy of the blueprint against his or her unfolding character by assessing the various virtues and vices. For the first seven
years of its life, the child passes through a period of *un*learning,
when what we might call the 'state of primal innocence' is
'unlearnt' through mimicking the actions of parents and others.
This is an interesting process because, of course, the child's
experience of certain parental attitudes is built into the blueprint
via the DNA, forming an integral part of the individual purpose.

In broader terms, these first seven years are marked by the
need for both stability and creativity. In diagrammatical form,
the energetic influences affecting the child are represented by
the triangle 9–1–8.

Between the ages of seven and fourteen, the further development of the force fields leads to increased glandular function
and more pronounced activity in the physical body. This corresponds to an expansion of the child's will and the onset of
puberty.

The next seven years, from age fourteen to twenty-one, is a
period in which the learning skills acquired during the first
fourteen years of life are fully consolidated. The subtle meridians or pathways of activity between the different energy centres

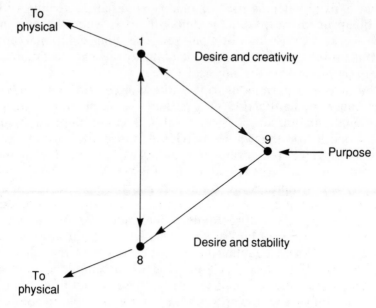

Figure 8   Energetic influences affecting the child: the first seven years

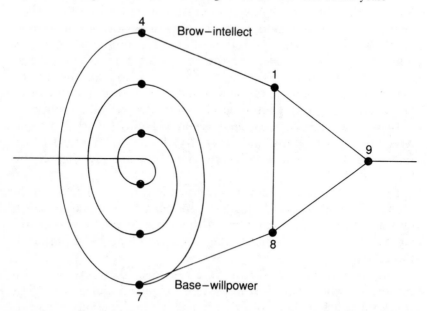

Figure 9   Energetic influences affecting the child: from seven to fourteen

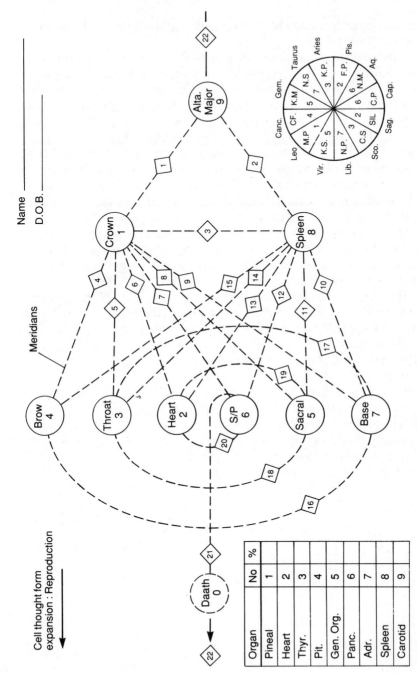

Figure 10 The sixty-four dimensions of causation

are developed, bringing to maturity the complete unfolding of the full blueprint.

These subtle meridians, of which there are twenty-two, provide a further active element to the blueprint. In the explanation accompanying Figure 3, it was pointed out that when the full number of energy centres (ten) is combined with the twenty-two meridians or pathways, we obtain the total of thirty-two. To take our explanation of the blueprint at work a stage further, these thirty-two energetic elements which form the force field around the body are the manifestation of the original thirty-two cells or dimensions encountered during the cleavage process following conception. By identifying and defining these elements that make up the creative force field of each individual, we have simultaneously established a method for measuring them. If we now take into account the bipolar activity of these centres, we arrive at the full sixty-four dimensions of causation present in each human being.

The total blueprint exists equally in every cell of the physical body and as a force field surrounding the body. Taken as a whole, its activity leads us to the symbol 0 in our diagram. This is the point which, viewed microcosmically – macrocosmically, represents respectively the wholeness of the next cell and next dimension of life.

Now that a formula has been established to determine the blueprint or purpose of life for an individual, the next step is to formulate a tangible system for decoding the information it contains. In evolving such a system, there are aspects from both metaphysics and the 'new' physics which together form an invaluable ground base for decoding the vital essence.

CHAPTER 3

The Vital Essence Decoded

If medicine is to justify fully its functional role as the 'art of healing' – that is, the 'art of making whole' – then it needs to embrace all three dimensions that make up the whole individual: the dimensions of purpose, mind, and body. Conventional modern Western medicine, having evolved in an essentially technological/scientific environment, naturally reasons that its largely allopathic systems of treatment are sound because they have a sound scientific basis. Furthermore, its remedial drugs are sound, too, for it demands that they are proven to be so by double-blind testing using modern technology and science.

Scientific proof is not everything, however, for science can only prove that which can be scientifically proven. It is possible for this reason that the scientific emphasis of modern medicine leads it largely to ignore its own origins in herbal medicine and the metaphysical sciences. These same traditions that link humanity in one way or another to the natural world and the cosmos, and laid the foundations for medicine as we now know it, are far from the minds of modern researchers and yet, to arrive at an all-encompassing method for healing disease, we must spread our sights wider than a purely scientific knowledge of the visible physical body.

In its quest for a comprehensive approach to healing, a truly 'three-dimensional' medicine must incorporate both the 'new' physical knowledge and the 'old' metaphysical knowledge. In this same context, 'complementary' medicine should perhaps not be considered merely as an amalgamation of alternative techniques to complement the scientific approach of orthodox medicine. It should be regarded more as an embracing of all dimensions of medicine that are complementary to the patient's requirements at the levels of purpose, mind and body. I am convinced that it is in bringing together these apparently diverse disciplines, and learning from the correspondences between them, that we shall come closer to understanding and decoding the vital essence within humanity.

METAPHYSICS

Metaphysics, which finds its expression in numerous ancient traditions, is often described as the science or philosophy of *being and knowing*. In the present context, we shall confine ourselves to a very brief examination of three main philosophies which suggest that attained life has both a pre-physical and a post-physical dimension; for where biology has provided us with our understanding of the physical DNA and its code, metaphysical knowledge points towards what we might call a 'subtle genetic code'. In other words, metaphysical theories about the purpose of life infer that the unseen causation of humanity perhaps knows its desires and aspirations in the form of a blueprint, which exists not only for individuals but for human races and civilisations as well.

It is the awareness of this underlying purpose of life that lies behind the mainstream of metaphysical thought, and behind each of the three philosophies we shall examine.

TIBETAN PHILOSOPHY

Tibetan philosophy favours the idea of inherited actions – that is, it sees humanity as experiencing during its current lifetime certain predetermined events. The nature of these events is based upon previous life experiences and the inherited activities of our forefathers while, at the same time, consideration is given to the needs of the world at this time and the role played by individuals in the evolution of the consciousness of the human race. This theory, known as *karma* holds that previous life experiences, and the way in which they were dealt with, will influence our reactions to possible similar events or to new trials to be faced in our continuing evolution. It is in this way that a dimension of purpose is added to life.

Many lines of modern thought, influenced by the mechanistic approach to science and medicine, perceive attained life as a process of evolution that runs from birth through puberty to maturity and adulthood, marriage and procreation, to end in death. At that point, what once had 'life' is regarded as descending for evermore into a void of absolute nothingness. Perhaps it is this particular perception of death as the absolute finality, followed by nothing, that has generated the Western fear of dying and, correspondingly, the frequent sensation of a total lack of purpose to life.

In my practice I meet many such people who come to me as patients. Their lack of purpose, however, is not confined to everyday life nor even to a definable period of their life; it extends to the thoughts of their goals and ambitions and, seemingly, coincides with their avoidance of examining the possible reason for their existence. And yet, it is this same lack of purpose that frequently leads to illness of one kind or another.

Illness in an individual often emanates from a lack of harmony between their intended direction or purpose in life and the direction they are actually pursuing. When this is the case, the events that befall them – for example, thwarted ambition, unrequited love, and so on – can set off a chain reaction of energetic imbalance which affects the functioning of their body at a cellular level. The reason for this is that *purpose* exists in every cell within the body, each one having its own role to play within the whole individual. Interference with the purpose of the whole will affect the purpose of the cell, and vice versa. In other words, imbalances of subtle energy flow cause over- or under-reaction within the electromagnetic force fields within cell structures, leading to illness or *dis*-ease of the system.

The Tibetan theory of subtle force fields considers the material physical body to be surrounded by force fields related to both mental and emotional activity. These force fields have the additional dimension of a number of energetic meridians that enter and leave the body through the various energy centres. These centres correspond to certain glands and organ systems referred to in Chapter 2 (see Chart 3, p.45).

When an imbalance occurs in the electromagnetic fields, energy centres or energetic meridians that make up the subtle systems surrounding the body, the reaction within the body will depend upon the attitude and aspirations manifested by the individual in dealing with the cause of the imbalance. Positive or negative reactions to stress, trauma and environmental conditions will influence the physical state of the organ, gland or system related to the particular energy centre involved.

Correct cell metabolism within the physical matter of the human body depends on an absolute clarity of thought with regard to the desired purpose of the individual blueprint which supplies the correct thought forms to attain mental clarity in dealing with daily stresses. These thoughts when known may be called upon at any time. I have known patients actually meditate upon their aspirations and general characteristics, as depicted by the blueprint. This clarity of thought influences both the current performance of each cell, and the endergonic process by which it produces a healthy replacement when its work is complete. From this it is possible to see how stress, worry and anxiety can interfere with normal cell metabolism and result in disease of the cells.

Tibetan philosophy regards mental and emotional stability as being of paramount importance. To help us achieve this, we should learn to react to all the incoming ideas and events of our life with a balance of logical thought, awareness and intuition, and we should deal with our problems with absolute mental clarity. At an emotional level we should enjoy the giving and receiving of love and wisdom, rather than becoming caught up in anger, envy, jealousy or revenge. In the Western world it is often emotional factors such as these that cause illness – for example, an individual may crave for additional material comforts far beyond their actual needs, only to suffer an emotional reaction when their desires are thwarted. Mental and emotional energy of this kind, when it becomes pent up at a pre-physical level, creates a predisposition for malignancies, infections and inflammatory physical conditions.

The principal thoughts of Tibetan philosophy are similar to those of another Eastern tradition, the *Ayurvedic* medicine of India.

THE AYURVEDIC PHILOSOPHY OF INDIA

Ayurveda is a holistic medical system which denies the separation of the physical form from the spiritual dimension in the way that is so much part and parcel of many Western theories. At the heart of Ayurvedic thought is the direct relationship between the macrocosm of the universe and the microcosm of man. According to this perception the one reflects, and is simultaneously always present within, the other. We are thus inextricably linked to our surroundings through the experience of all our senses (our inbuilt system of communication with the 'outside' world), but in particular our sense of awareness. Many of these senses are employed far below their intended level. For example, how much attention do we really pay to the impressions conveyed to us through our senses of hearing, smell and taste? Much of the deterioration in our sensory awareness and, ultimately, our quality of life is due to a near-continuous barrage of excessive stimulation from technological apparatus eroding the finer levels of everyday awareness and perception. Through our Western preoccupation with the pursuit of material luxuries and an increasing dependence on technological methods of communication, we are losing our awareness of the deeper, more intimate relationship we share with the world around us.

According to *Ayurveda* the balance and well-being of humanity depends upon three major cosmological forces – the *tridoshas* – which control all bodily and mental activity. Classical Ayurvedic texts describe the three forces (called in Sanskrit *pitta*, *kapha* and *vata*) through an analogy in which humanity stands upon the earth as part of the animal, vegetable and mineral kingdoms, interconnected with the sun, moon and wind, or alternatively, fire, water and air.

The sun (*pitta*) radiates heat and provides the energy of the lifeforce, as well as the energy necessary for all physiochemical and biochemical processes, digestion, cellular metabolism, etc.

The moon (*kapha*) acts upon the biological rhythms. It rules the tides and has an affinity with water, the element that cools and promotes the flow of life-giving fluid. It also gives form to the cells of the body, lubricates the joints, and visibly affects the equilibrium of fluids in body tissue and organs.

The wind (*vata*) moves the atmosphere and is the source of

movement in humanity, providing impulses to our complex nervous system and giving us the will to move and create.

Ayurveda also considers that all matter, both animate and inanimate, is a composite whole made from the five elements of earth, water, fire, air and ether. This essential frame of reference in Indian thought permits an all-encompassing view of the many relationships that link man to his surroundings. In this respect, like much other traditional Eastern thought, *Ayurveda* possibly bears a closer resemblance to modern psychotherapy than to 'pure' religion or philosophy. It is therefore not surprising that many complementary medical bodies show an increasing interest in what is generally regarded as Eastern 'mysticism'.

Holistic concerns lie at the heart of Ayurvedic medicine, one of the oldest known medical systems. In its treatment of man as a complex whole related to his environment, the chief methods it employs for the maintenance of health and the fulfilment of life are diets and medicinal herbs. The use of the latter stems from a profound understanding of the relationship that exists between man and the plant kingdom, for both have the same forces at work within them and both are created from the same building blocks of existence. In fact, the pharmocopoeia of Indian medicine contains many remedies which are accurately detailed in their action of re-establishing order within the patient and his or her place in the environment.

At one time, the only available drugs were substances extracted from plants or, in some cases, animals. Herbalism, the study and use of plants with known medicinal value, was practised by the Chinese more than 5000 years ago, and still thrives in many parts of the world.

CHINESE PHILOSOPHY

Chinese philosophy or *Taoism* views life as cyclic and is based upon the idea that life fluctuates in a continuous cyclical rhythm. This fluctuating rhythm, which the Chinese consider to be the fundamental rhythm of the universe, is the product of two archetypal poles, *Yin* and *Yang*, that set the limits for the cycles of change. It is basic to Chinese thought that *Yang*, having reached its zenith, retreats in favour of *Yin*, and *Yin*, on reaching its zenith, declines in favour of *Yang*.

Polarity exists in all things. Modern science has proved that all occurrences of energy – whether in generated electricity or in the energetic potential of cells – depend upon polarity (expressed in Western terminology as positive and negative). All manifestation is generated by the interplay of these two archetypal poles, and modern physics has confirmed that just such a dynamic of polarity must exist before there can be living matter.

The *Yin* (negative) – *Yang* (positive) polarity of Chinese philosophy expresses itself in the dynamic balance of opposites: for example, moon – sun, earth – heaven, night – day, winter – summer, female – male, and so on. However, nothing is ever solely *Yin* or *Yang*, negative or positive – a concept that is often difficult for Western thought to comprehend. According to Chinese thought, the harmony we refer to as 'good' is to be found in the dynamic balance of these two opposite poles. It is the disharmony that arises from their imbalance which is 'bad' or harmful.

The progression of thought for the individual and the evolution of the human race (or individual races) as a whole is produced by the ceaseless cosmic process of motion through change and activity. No particular 'force' is used in any aspect of Chinese medicine; it purely redirects or activates the cyclic energies inherent in man and the universe. The Chinese name for this cyclic energy is *Ch'i*, which flows through meridians or pathways within the body. The free flow of *Ch'i* is necessary for health and this is achieved by stimulating points on the meridians. These meridians, documented over thousands of years, are the energy systems in the physical body.

According to the principles of Chinese medicine, disease manifests when the body becomes unbalanced and *Ch'i* fails to flow correctly. The causes of these imbalances are many – poor diet, lack of sleep or exercise, disharmony at a mental or emotional level arising from tensions in family, social or working life, and so on.

There appears to be much within metaphysical philosophies that provides a base for the investigation of an equivalent phenomenon to the DNA code existing at a subtle level, prior to physical manifestation. There are also many profound aspects of ancient teachings that coincide with proven facets of modern scientific theory. The thread of absolute truth running simultaneously through both the metaphysical and physical sciences becomes apparent when we consider that metaphysical knowledge of the life-support glands and their related consciousness finds its physical correspondence in the amino acids of the DNA which, in turn, concurs with the twenty-two pathways between the thought or energy centres.

THE SCIENCE OF PHYSICS

If there exists somewhere a blueprint or plan of assembly for the developing embryo with the necessary instructions required to achieve the finished form, then it is worth considering that the strong element of teleology or purpose involved directs the living organism towards its final stage of development according to some cosmic plan. The existence of such a blueprint of tangible thought at a pre-physical level would contain clues not only to the aspirations and types of individuals but also the predisposition of individuals to particular ailments. We may ask ourselves, for example, if there is a connection between the emotion of fear and the secretion of the hormone epinephrine by the adrenal glands as a stimulant for the 'fight or flight' system. If there is, why, at the touch of a thought, is non-matter transformed into matter? Again, we may ask why does the experience of stress or anxiety manifest itself as an asthmatic attack that disables the respiration of a normally healthy individual?

We have already examined certain aspects of metaphysical thought in connection with the subtle levels of human existence, but in order to shed further corroborative light on the pre-physical levels of humanity, we now turn to the current scientific thinking of quantum physics.

New physics tells us that the paper on which these words are printed is not solid. What holds true for the hydrogen atoms of wood pulp also applies to the atoms in the cells of our bodies. The subatomic particles that constitute these atoms are separated from one another by relatively great distances. Analogously, when we look up at the night sky we see millions of stars separated by immense distances and, likewise, the particles of our body have considerable space between them. How can we reconcile our perception of the human body as a solid material form with the vast reaches of emptiness it actually comprises? To understand this important question, we need to consider it from the quantum perspective – that only a shadowy line separates an observable particle from a wave form, and the human body from a non-physical body. This quantum phenomenon of wave/particle duality is encountered in the observation of light.

The fact that white light is composed of separate wave lengths of light becomes apparent when a ray of white light passes through a prism and is broken up into the seven colours of the spectrum. Similarly, the light from an incandescent light bulb has its own spectrum of wave lengths generated by the electric current passing through the tungsten filament. An interesting phenomenon occurs when we use a dimmer switch to control the amount of light emanating from the filament. If we turn the dimmer lower and lower until only the smallest amount of light is emitted, it will emanate as a *particle* of light and not as a wave form. Of course, such an experiment is not possible in the everyday reality of our own homes. Physicists, however, can broadcast light to show actual grains (or photons) of light. Photons are produced by the collision between the flow of moving electrons in the electricity and the electrons whirling in orbit around the tungsten atom. Because the photon cannot be reduced to smaller particles, it is called a *quantum* of light – a *quantum* (*Latin* 'how much') being an indivisible unit of discrete energy.

The photon as such has no real mass, and yet it can be regarded as a particle. This is the shadowy world of quantum physics in which non-matter can transform into matter, time into space, mass into energy, and vice versa. Like the emotion of fear and the epinephrine molecule, however, light cannot be observed simultaneously as a wave and a photon – it is either the one or the other. And yet the light bulb itself remains a constant. It does not exist in one reality to emit waves and another to emit particles: in the shadowy quantum dimension of nature, transformation manifests within the boundaries of the same reality.

What exactly happens in this shadowy dimension is not

known. Whether we are a physicist or doctor of medicine, we can no more determine when photons become light waves than we can subdivide the body to arrive at the point where thought turns into a molecule. In this context, perhaps the seemingly mysterious spontaneous remissions from incurable illness can be understood as the imprint or communication of thoughts triggering change in the physical body – and perhaps these thoughts emanate from a blueprint for the individual human being, similar to a genetic code, but existing at a pre-physical level.

For many of us the idea of communication, which we can also describe as 'action at a distance', may mean little more than telephoning someone on the other side of the world, sending a fax to a company in another town or city, or receiving images on our television screens from a distant satellite. The marvel of modern workaday communications technology may even have led us to attribute to technologists the invention of what is essentially a naturally occurring phenomenon. Its presence in the natural world is easy to overlook or take for granted, even though we may feel the heat of the sun's rays, or watch the rise and fall of the sea tides in response to the gravitational pull of the moon. It is also easier to understand the existence of communication or action at a distance when it involves the vast expanse of space between planets than the relatively invisible distances that separate particles at a subatomic level. However, in the present context, it is the latter that is really of interest because of its relevance for the world of medicine.

In the world of subatomic physics, it has been found that electrons accelerated towards each other at high velocity do not collide. Instead, they perform what the physicists call 'scattering'; that is, as they approach each other an electric repulsive charge occurs and they change direction without making contact. The process is not unlike a speeded-up film of two columns of ants criss-crossing as they march in opposite directions. Somehow they are alerted to the other's presence so that when their paths cross they pass each other without colliding. In the subatomic world a 'messenger' particle, the *photon*, is exchanged between the two electrons, impelling them to change direction and thus avoid the impending collision. In this area of quantum fuzziness, it is not clear which electron sends the message and which receives it; just as it is unclear when and how the experienced emotion of fear creates the epinephrine molecule.

What is clear is that the objective measurements of modern physicists have indisputably shown the twin phenomena of action at a distance and an existing awareness between the seen and unseen, thus confirming many centuries of subjective thinking by metaphysicists with regard to the action of universal thought upon form. As a result we now know that action at a distance permeates the whole of the electromagnetic force fields of the cells within the body, as well as the surrounding field of the physical form.

The particular phenomenon of action or communication over a great distance is confirmed by the EPR (Einstein–Podolski–Rosen) experiment. This experiment causes two electrons, identified as #1 and #2, to be balanced so that the total spin is zero. The electrons are then separated very rapidly over a great distance. After a long period of time (a light year) measurements are performed upon one of the electrons.

> However, the EPR experiment shows the interaction of the observer with the observed in quantum mechanics can have *non-local* effects. If we grant . . . that the observation of electron #1 brings into existence some property, say, the z- or x-component [axis] of the spin – then this observation brings into existence the same property of electron #2 which is a light year away. Furthermore, this property of electron #2 is brought into existence at the instant the measurement is performed on electron #1, even though no information about the measurement, no forces and no influence of any kind can reach electron #2 for at least a year. There appears to be instantaneous action at a distance.
>
> (Quoted from *the Anthropic Cosmological Principle*, John D. Barrow and Frank J. Tipler, Oxford University Press 1986, page 463.)

The unexplained component in the EPR experiment that shows that, in quantum mechanics, the interaction of the observer with the observed can have non-local effects is of great significance for the world of medicine and we shall be referring to it again in Chapter 4 in connection with blood tests.

THE TWENTY-TWO SUBTLE MERIDIANS OR THOUGHT STRINGS

It is phenomena such as those we have just described, along with the existence of a blueprint of purpose at a subtle level, that need to be taken into consideration in formulating a new biological model for the human form. We can decode this blueprint or vital essence of the human form using the formula suggested in Chapter 2 (see p. 37) and all that now remains to be added to our formula are the twenty-two pathways or subtle meridians of thought form that connect the energy centres of the physical body, thus providing the component for 'action at a distance'. Before doing so, however, it is worth noting that the nine energy centres and the categories associated with them (described in the previous chapter) relate to *states* of consciousness, whilst the meridians and the flow of energetic thought along them are essentially related to *developing* consciousness.

The translation of the subtle meridians into diagrammatic form can be seen in Figure 10 (p. 61) in which a meridian connects the force fields of energy centres 9 and 1 (Meridian 1), 9 and 8 (Meridian 2), 1 and 8 (Meridian 3), and so forth.

In Chapter 2, we established the percentages for the different categories in the blueprint for Richard Mason (see p. 43). These too can now be interpreted in diagrammatic form, along with the activity of the subtle meridians necessary to fulfil the required aspiration during the life time of Richard and, in particular, their connection with the development of the virtues of Category 6, the primary area of aspiration within the quadrant of Purpose and Aspiration of the cosmological diagram. (Note that categories 5 and 9 do not appear in the quadrant of Purpose and Aspiration.) Together these elements make up the desired blueprint. (See Figure 7, p. 43.)

This information regarding the subtle meridians and energy centre consciousness could also be written as follows, with the circles indicating categories, and the squares indicating meridians:

$$⑨—◇1◇—①—◇7◇—⑥—◇12◇—⑧—◇2◇—⑨$$

This format represents a cyclic meridian of subtle energy existing as thought form within the universal order which, when activated within Richard's consciousness, would bring into play the aspirations of his life's blueprint. The use of the tangible thought forms existing on the meridians enables the natural innate healing energy and consciousness to circulate through the energy centres that control the glandular system of the physical body. This in turn provides for correct cellular metabolism at a physical level and correct consciousness at both mental and emotional levels.

As the energy centres themselves are vital in allowing the natural flow of energy from centre to centre, it is essential that their activation follows a pattern or plan that is complementary to the desired blueprint, thus allowing the aspirations and the subtle DNA to manifest as part of a harmonious universal process. The deliberately premature 'opening up' or overstimulation of certain centres out of sequence can sometimes seriously interfere with the natural progression of the unfolding blueprint. When incorrect thought forms lead to blockages or imbalances in the meridians or energy centres, this can be remedied by medicinal means and by the patient's own conscious thought processes. Regarding the latter, as will be seen from the following descriptions of the twenty-two meridians, the patient's own mental and emotional attitudes can be instrumental in maintaining the correct flow of energetic thought along the meridians.

Meridian 1

Linkage   Centre 9 (Purpose; Alta Major; Carotid Plexus) and Centre 1 (Will and Power; Crown; Pineal).
Principal characteristics   Positive 'male' energy instigating new initiatives and new developments.

This meridian is connected with the new and important cycles or events in one's life. At such times there is often the need for varying degrees of adaptability, versatility, tact, diplomacy, and the display of more self-confidence. We must also be prepared to take calculated risks and show initiative. The latter, when correctly used, can lead to success and the overcoming of known obstacles.

Those who display hesitation and the inability to face reality will be helped to overcome their weakness of will and 'lack of nerve' by the positive thoughts induced into the subtle body through this meridian and its related energy centre activity.

Meridian 2

Linkage Centre 9 (Purpose: Alta Major; Carotid Plexus) and Centre 8 (Physical Purpose and Desire; Spleen; Spleen).
Principal characteristics Creative 'female' energy – the source of intuition and insight.

Meridian 2 is instrumental in releasing hidden knowledge from the subconscious mind, thus activating one's intuition to bring forward ideas and possible solutions for current problems and giving strength and hope for the future. There are times in our lives when we need to listen to sound advice, whether it comes from our intuition (the inner voice) or via an outside source. It is therefore significant that this meridian is positively influenced by contact with a woman of wisdom for it is also the source of creative talent (i.e. the Muse) of the artist and innovator.

As part of the healing process, an appreciation of art and beauty can act through Meridian 2 to help overcome emotional difficulties. The correct flow of energetic thought may become impaired by a rigidity of mind and a reluctance to take advice. Alternatively, the flow along this meridian may be weakened when we are diverted from our true path in life by the strong convictions of another – a state which is often indicated when a weak male is under the dominant influence of a female.

Meridian 3

Linkage Centre 8 (Physical Purpose and Desire; Spleen; Spleen) and Centre 1 (Will and Power; Crown; Pineal).
Principal characteristics Fertility and growth, with stability.

This meridian is related to growth and the establishment of firm foundations for individuals and families alike. It provides the female with fertility, fruitfulness and the blessings of sound motherhood, and also aids domestic stability in that it provides us all with the knowledge, reassurance and protection from outside influences that we generally associate with maternal care. The activity of this meridian is also apparent when there is a strong affection for the world of nature. At those times when we need to progress in our personal lives, this meridian gives us the support we require.

For those who are experiencing domestic upheaval or over-protectiveness, this meridian can help re-establish harmony and balance. It will also help those who view the universe as impersonal or malevolent. One beneficial way of correcting the thought forms of this meridian is by forging closer contact with the plant and animal kingdoms.

Meridian 4

Linkage   Centre 1 (Will and Power; Crown; Pineal) and Centre 4 (Harmony out of Sacrifice or Conflict; Brow; Pituitary).
Principal characteristics   Authority and ambition, with self-control.

Meridian 4 links the crown and brow centres, bringing balance between our rational and creative thought processes and between the material and spiritual worlds. It also instils equilibrium between the left and right hemispheres of the brain, thus enhancing our willpower and providing us with authority, ambition and self-control.

Sometimes our inability to learn from life's experiences may result in immature reactions, subservience, or even a sense of resignation due to thwarted ambitions. When this is the case, this meridian and its inherent thoughts can be used to induce creative energy and the ability to understand the lessons of life. It is also useful for the male lacking in confidence or authority as it will give him integrity and sound judgement.

Meridian 5

Linkage   Centre 1 (Will and Power; Crown; Pineal) and Centre 3 (Higher Active Intelligence; Throat; Thyroid).
Principal characteristics   Wisdom and good counsel; spirituality.

As this meridian links two centres related to higher knowledge, it provides us with spiritual insight and good counsel. When we begin to question the situations that are presented to us in life, rather than blindly accepting them, the free flow of knowledge along Meridian 5 reveals much that may have been previously hidden from us. Being a source of enlightened wisdom, it is beneficial for those who are teachers.

At those times when we suffer from inner loneliness the thought energy of this meridian brings us freedom from restrictive practices and comfort through religious or spiritual activities. Sometimes this state may persist, manifesting symptoms of mental or emotional anguish. When this occurs, counselling may help to re-establish the correct flow of energetic thought.

Meridian 6

Linkage Centre 1 (Will and Power; Crown; Pineal) and Centre 2 (Love and Wisdom; Heart; Thymus).
Principal characteristics Choices; intuitive insights; moral integrity.

The flashes of insight or ideas that resolve current problems just at the crucial moment emanate from this meridian. By linking the intuition with love and wisdom, it provides us with the inner voice we should listen to when faced with choices of an emotional nature. Contrary to what our logical mind might tell us, in order to arrive at the correct decision we should use intuition rather than intellect, and inspiration rather than reason. Patience and caution can safeguard us from the impetuosity which is sometimes mistakenly taken for inspired spontaneity.

It is often all too easy to allow our decisions to be made solely according to desire or temptation. High moral standards are needed for successful progression along our path in life and the opening of the linked centres. Meridian 6 promotes the integrity and maturity necessary to keep us from making decisions that will divert us from our true purpose.

Meridian 7

Linkage Centre 1 (Will and Power; Crown; Pineal) and Centre 6 (Devotion and Digestion; Solar Plexus; Pancreas).

Principal characteristics   Self-esteem; the will to succeed.

The degree to which we are successful in life, at whatever level, corresponds directly to the degree of our appropriate commitment – for example, obstacles are successfully overcome through perseverance and hard work, and material success is based upon personal endeavours. This meridian provides the energetic thoughts of truth, accuracy and personal effort necessary for the real success in life that extends beyond a superficial level.

For the fruitful development of Meridian 7, we should work to become aware of the true quality of life. If we rely solely on others for financial help, or on some inherited fortune, our own sense of relative values and will to succeed may suffer. We must be attentive to the needs of those around us and not ride roughshod over them, nor try to obtain our own way by force.

Meridian 8

Linkage   Centre 1 (Will and Power; Crown; Pineal) and Centre 5 (Intellect and Procreation; Sacral; Gonads).
Principal characteristics   Truth; justice; integrity.

Truth and integrity based upon a combination of intuition and concrete knowledge flow along this meridian, providing us with the ability to arbitrate or arrive at a mutually satisfactory agreement through negotiation. It also gives us the ability to listen to and take into account the needs of others before acting or giving advice, and its energy can give us much-needed hope and peace when we experience fear or worry.

If our general conduct and attitude towards our fellow human beings and the world at large lack the necessary balance of moral justice, illness may emanate from the centres related to the activity of this meridian. The manifestation of such related illnesses would indicate the need for a reappraisal of ourselves and our integrity in relation to others.

Meridian 9

Linkage   Centre 1 (Will and Power; Crown; Pineal) and Centre 7 (Physical Will and Excretion; Base; Adrenal).
Principal characteristics   The inner voice; discretion; the need for silence.

The energetic flow of this meridian opens up the way for the voice of the inner self to be heard. The developing awareness of our inner voice is accompanied by the sensation of hidden qualities of knowledge awakening from within us. When this occurs we should withdraw from any restrictive practices or actions in order for new developments to acquire their appropriate form; it is certainly not a time to stumble headlong into further problems. If anything, we should take things more slowly, possibly seeking help from a wise counsellor or practising silent meditation. When new degrees of patience and tolerance are attained, the flow of inner wisdom and knowledge will increase.

In the normal noise and bustle of our daily lives it is often difficult to hear the 'still small voice'. Nevertheless, we should wait and listen for its guidance. Those who refuse to do so may experience a detrimental change in their affairs or perhaps witness the collapse of their ambitions.

Meridian 10

Linkage   Centre 8 (Physical Purpose and Desire; Spleen; Spleen) and Centre 7 (Physical Will and Excretion; Base; Adrenal).
Principal characteristics   Destiny; new beginnings.

This is the meridian of destiny and new beginnings in our lives and daily affairs. When destiny takes a hand it appears as though the events which happen to us are unaffected by any influence we may attempt to exert over them and, by the same token, our problems seemingly solve themselves. This is also the meridian by which we reap what we sow, benefiting from good deeds carried out in the past. However, where destiny is concerned, only the passage of time reveals the true course of events.

Meridian 11

Linkage Centre 8 (Physical Purpose and Desire; Spleen; Spleen) and Centre 5 (Intellect and Procreation; Sacral; Gonads).
Principal characteristics Strength and moral courage; reconciliation.

The flow of energy along Meridian 11 furnishes us with the courage and strength to take risks in the material world, blessed by the world of the spirit, thus giving us the opportunity to put plans into action. The ability to achieve genuine success in the material world also stems from our own state of personal harmony, the attainment of which necessitates overcoming any immoral tendencies and reconciling ourselves with our enemies. The latter can either be related to outside events or to the unruly elements within ourselves.

Real opportunities always contain an element of risk of one kind or another, for which strong nerves and moral courage are essential. Our own conscious input of these two qualities will facilitate the flow of similar energies along this meridian.

Meridian 12

Linkage Centre 8 (Physical Purpose and Desire; Spleen; Spleen) and Centre 6 (Devotion and Digestion; Solar Plexus; Pancreas).
Principal characteristics Flexibility in a time of drastic change.

When inner knowledge and wisdom from the unconscious mind are brought forth via Meridian 12, it indicates a willingness to subject oneself to the dictates of the inner self. This last factor, of itself, heralds a time of change (perhaps even of a drastic nature such as a change of career) and therefore this meridian also provides us with the flexibility of mind to adapt to whatever changes may occur. When the time is exactly right for the desired change to take place, we may find ourselves casting aside practical and material considerations, sensing intuitively that we shall be able to take the outcome in our stride, whatever it may be.

In the course of our life we may sometimes be faced with

an apparently unpleasant change but, however undesirable the change may initially appear to be, it is perhaps the change we *need* to make in order for us to progress along our path. Non-acceptance of such a change, or the refusal to adapt to a change that has already taken place, may prove to be a regressive step in the long term.

Meridian 13

Linkage Centre 8 (Physical Purpose and Desire; Spleen; Spleen) and Centre 2 (Love and Wisdom; Heart; Thymus).
Principal characteristics Major changes – 'off with the old life and on with the new'.

The changes that happen in our lives occur for a variety of reasons. Sometimes they are a natural but necessary way of leaving behind that which is outmoded or superfluous to our current requirements, so that we can proceed into the future unencumbered by the excess baggage of our past. If our reluctance to change leaves us clinging to things we have outgrown, whether these are people, material possessions or ideas, an enforced change may be necessary so that our attachment to them can be curtailed.

As with the previous meridian, when we react positively to change, however unexpected or undesirable it may seem to be, we take a step forward on our own evolutionary path.

Meridian 14

Linkage Centre 8 (Physical Purpose and Desire; Spleen; Spleen) and Centre 3 (Higher Active Intelligence; Throat; Thyroid).
Principal characteristics Skilful control of self and others, leading to harmonious partnerships.

The energetic flow of this meridian enables us to exercise skilful control over volatile factors in both our personal and workaday lives. It is important, however, to remember that what we see as occurring in the world outside us is also, to some extent, a mirror image of what is taking place at an inner level in ourselves, and vice versa. When we skilfully combine the talents of others we are simultaneously making progress for ourselves and, by the same reasoning, through carefully exercising self-control, we avoid the temptation merely to manipulate people and situations to our own selfish advantage.

Meridian 15

Linkage Centre 8 (Physical Purpose and Desire; Spleen; Spleen) and Centre 4 (Harmony out of Sacrifice or Conflict; Brow; Pituitary).
Principal characteristics The fine balance between harmony and discord is controlled by the balance between intuition and logic, or the subconscious and conscious levels of the mind.

The energy flow of this meridian needs to be handled with care and caution. On the one hand, it inclines the subconscious mind to dominate logical and discriminative thinking; on the other, it can cause the repression of our intuitive powers by the intellect, resulting in a high level of left-brain activity. When the latter is not kept in balance by our intuition, or by self-control governed by instinct rather than logic, it can work to our own detriment, causing a lust for power, greed, and the temptation to ride roughshod over others, especially those who appear to stand in our way by not sharing our own particular approach to things or view of the world. In brief, an incorrect flow of energy along Meridian 15 can turn harmony to discord. When this happens it can be regarded as something of a blessing in disguise, for it reminds us that we ignore the deeper levels of our existence at our peril.

Meridian 16

Linkage: Centre 4 (Harmony out of Sacrifice or Conflict; Brow; Pituitary) and Centre 7 (Physical Will and Excretion; Base; Adrenal).
Principal characteristics: Destiny; suffering and/or difficulties.

It is often difficult for us to come to terms with suffering – whether it is our own, that of those close to us, or that of the wider world – because it usually strikes us as being either un-warranted, unnecessary or unjust. When we are directly or indirectly affected by suffering it is of little consolation to be told that it is 'for a reason', or due to 'the forces of destiny' – and yet both of these explanations hold the key to us becoming free from its effects. Sometimes we can lose sight of the distinction between suffering and pity or self-pity, particularly when our emotions become involved. Viewed in a wider context, all events occur for one reason or another and it is our willingness to face their reality, and the reality of their consequences, that leads to progress and evolution in life. It is here that willpower and logic can be used consciously to turn suffering into a positive force for good, thus providing a corrective flow of energetic thought along this meridian.

Meridian 17

Linkage: Centre 7 (Physical Will and Excretion; Base; Pancreas) and Centre 3 (Higher Active Intelligence; Throat; Thyroid).
Principal characteristics: Fulfilment; insight into new horizons.

Meridian 17 provides us with insights into future possibilities, thus widening the horizons of our ideals and ambitions and offering us the potential of both renewed hope and fulfilment. When we are faced with a panoramic view of this kind our adaptability is put to the test, and we may even need to cast aside a rigid state of mind in order to expand beyond our all-too-familiar old boundaries. The opportunities offered at such times should be carefully considered with a positive view to taking them up, for although each opportunity may appear to occur at an essentially material level, it also has another, less obvious side to it that forms an integral part of our own individual evolution. Perhaps it is an opportunity to overcome self-doubt or a reluctance to accept. It may even give us the opportunity to trust others again, and so learn that not all help is offered for reasons of self-interest or reward.

Meridian 18

Linkage: Centre 3 (Higher Active Intelligence; Throat; Thyroid) and Centre 5 (Intellect and Procreation; Sacral; Gonads).
Principal characteristics: Crisis; intuition versus the logical mind.

This meridian is active in times of crisis, particularly during those crises that arise when our faith or beliefs are profoundly questioned. Here again we encounter an apparent conflict between our intuitive and logical minds. On the one hand the use of our intuition, inner knowledge and spirituality can lead us forward into the next stage of our path in life whilst, on the other, reason can inhibit our progress. When we stop to think things over 'consciously' and in a logical manner we can often lose our nerve. 'Consciousness', however has nothing to do with what we normally call 'thinking', and everything to do with using the power and energy of thought. One possible way to resolve our various problems and/or crises is to listen first to our intuition and then, when the time is right, to use our logical mind and willpower to help us put what we need to do into effect. It is more than likely that our problem or crisis was produced by the action of our logical mind, and had we followed our intuition in the first place it might never have arisen.

Meridian 19

Linkage: Centre 5 (Intellect and Procreation; Sacral; Gonads) and Centre 2 (Love and Wisdom; Heart; Thymus).
Principal characteristics: Imagination and daring; positive action.

Imagination and daring are necessary in situations where the odds against us appear to be overwhelming. They can also help us to find our way out of a lengthy period of trouble. Action of a positive and daring kind can bring us unexpected but well-earned rewards; however, we need to be careful not to use our imagination and daring in too reckless a manner. If we do, we run the risk of creating a fantasy world for ourselves, rather than attaining any real and worthwhile goals. This is where a clear intellect and sound reasoning come into their own, because, in enabling us to see the practicalities or impracticalities of our proposed course of action, they help us to avoid any possible pitfalls.

Meridian 20

Linkage: Centre 2 (Love and Wisdom; Heart; Thymus) and Centre 6 (Devotion and Digestion; Solar Plexus; Pancreas).
Principal characteristics: The joy and pleasure of a new lease of life.

The energetic flow of this meridian gives us enjoyment from even the smallest things in life, enabling us to appreciate fully the world of nature, and to experience a joyous and justified pleasure in our own achievements and those of others, however small these may be. The sense of expansion this gives us is like a new lease of life, sometimes taking the form of a return to long-term health based upon a strong immune system. When we experience life stirring within us in this manner, we should not waste the opportunities that may come our way to use our newly raised state of consciousness to attain new heights of endeavour.

The flow of energy along this meridian can be stimulated by a conscious enjoyment and appreciation of life.

Meridian 21

Linkage: Centre 6 (Devotion and Digestion; Solar Plexus; Pancreas) and *Daath*.
Principal characteristics: The culmination of current events and the end of a cycle of destiny.

Meridian 21 is the final and successful completion of any matter at hand, or the culmination of events and the ending of a cycle of destiny. It leads us towards *Daath*, the centre with no symbol and the point at which the masculine and feminine are united and indivisible. *Daath*, regarded by some to be the tenth centre of the hidden or unrevealed cosmic mind, is deemed invisible, but its existence is indicated by the meridian leading towards its centre. It is the sphere of activity where, at a microscopic level, the memory bank of centres and meridian activity previously attained in cellular reproduction culminates as pure force and takes on form for the reproduction of the next cell.

Daath is also the highest point of human awareness and the culmination of the nine energy centres of the subtle body. Seen as the bridge for the journey to the next dimension, it expresses the idea of the 'next step' once our path in life is complete, and represents the point of choice between further evolution in other spheres or remaining and assisting the planetary hierarchy.

Meridian 22

Linkage: *Daath* and Centre 9 (Purpose; Alta Major; Carotid Plexus).
Principal characteristics: Completion and progression to higher attainment.

At the material level of cellular reproduction, Meridian 22 continues the flow of knowledge and intelligence for the reproduction of further cells in the physical body. At the highest level, it is the path upon which the incoming soul travels to create the trinity of essence, male (positive polarity), and female (negative polarity), at the point of conception in the physical world. The essence, activated by pure force, determines the blueprint for the path of the soul during its life on earth and for the physical body necessary for its journey.

Through Meridian 22, *karma* from the past is programmed into the ten energy centres and twenty-two meridians that together constitute the thirty-two dimensions of creative activity in the subtle anatomy of the human form. This subtle activity has its physical counterpart in the process of cleavage, during which the one fertilized egg becomes transformed into a foetal ball of thirty-two cells prior to its implantation on the uterine wall. At different levels, and in more senses than one, the old cycle is complete and another begins.

The name I use to refer to the system of medicine based on the blueprint formula and its related components is *Base 64*, which is derived from the fact that when we take into account the positive and negative polarities of these thirty-two subtle dimensions of activity, we arrive at sixty-four dimensions for potential healing. The term 'system', however, should not be interpreted in its narrower sense. Base 64 is a flexible 'system' which can either be used as a whole or in part, with the practitioner using one or more of the various components in conjunction with their own particular method of healing or therapy.

CHAPTER 4

Symptoms of Disorder

Where the cause of illness is concerned, conventional medical practice subscribes to the germ theory: specific diseases are caused by specific microbes. Such a theory is very much in keeping with the traditional view that the living organism functions like a machine; when a breakdown occurs the cause can be traced to a malfunctioning part. Admittedly, this theory of specific disease causation has been successful where certain acute infectious processes are concerned, but it is also worth considering that some kind of depletion in the immune system must first exist before the process of infection is able to begin.

We can expand on this idea of the cause-behind-the-cause by saying that in order to understand the real cause of illness in an individual, we should first endeavour to understand the cause of the human form. If we are able to establish a workable model or formula for the latter, we will also arrive at an understanding of the former. To examine this further we shall explore the differences between an orthodox or medical diagnosis and a diagnosis based on the principles of subtle causation.

THE PATIENT — THE CAUSES AND EFFECTS OF HEALTH AND ILLNESS

'Energy follows thought.' This familiar saying embodies the idea that every material object or phenomenon begins its existence as a thought, which, through its translation into energetic actions, comes into manifestation (thought being the fundamental and predominant factor in deciding what has been and what is, as well as what will be the inspiring factor for the future). This same view regards thought, or the deeper conscious processes, as being the fundamental causative factor of both health and illness, order and disorder. In turn, thought itself can be regarded as an individual or localized phenomenon (as in the case of the individual human being), or as being of a large-scale collective nature (as with the universal mind, or universal order), or both, with the former being an integral part of the latter.

In each human being there is a continual dynamic energy exchange between the subconscious and conscious minds and the physical body, the body being the physical vehicle of expression for this exchange. If we were able to see it, the vital essence of every living person is reflected at each and every moment through this vehicle, thus bringing it into the dimensions of time and space. However, not all of the innermost processes are allowed to manifest in this way for we control how others see us through the action of free will.

In the course of a consultation many patients will apparently give freely of themselves, but only at the level of their personality. Much remains hidden beneath this surface level because the energy and expression that make up an individual's deeper levels of consciousness are often suppressed. Not that this is necessarily intentional. More often than not it occurs inadvertently, so many practitioners learn to read the language of the physical body in order to understand what its actions and movements are telling us about the patient.

A significant part of the process of attaining health and harmony involves allowing the totality of our vital essence to express itself through our personality. Although these two aspects of our being – in effect, the inner and outer – are inseparable, it is necessary at this stage to make a distinction between our personality and our vital essence, so that their potential harmony and the physical health this engenders can be more fully understood. Furthermore, this interaction between the different levels within each human being is relevant to the three dimensions of purpose, mind and body, in that the manifestation of illness in the physical body can have its cause at the levels of mind or purpose.

Allopathic medicine has examined the dense physical body

down to its minutest particle of matter but has shown only a passing interest in the mental and emotional states of the patient. And yet, if we consider that all manifestation can be viewed as wave form or particle, then it becomes increasingly apparent that the manifestation of health and harmony emanates from the level of purpose and the blueprint of the vital essence via the mind, for these subtle energetic wave forms are inseparable from the particles of the dense physical body. If we are to have harmony in the physical vehicle, then we must also have harmony at a mental level – and this will only happen when the mind is truly expressing the energies of our vital essence and purpose.

The mental activity of each of us reacts and responds in a discriminative way to the impact of thoughts and ideas emanating from the purpose within us, or from sources outside ourselves. It is a process of logical and discriminative thinking in which the mind chooses either to learn from or reject the ideas that are placed before it. The reactions of the mind are vital in that they should result in a continuing mental awareness, as well as a further longing for clarity of thought and the acquisition of intelligent and enquiring processes of thought. This integrated process creates a balanced harmonious mental activity which is capable of dealing with any situation we may encounter. But what happens when the mental attitude developed by an individual is confronted with an idea or thought from an internal or external source and reacts in a manner that is contrary to the attitude required by the purpose or vital essence? The following examples may help to illustrate this point.

Let's say that a man in a managerial position is offered a directorship. He secretly lacks confidence in himself, feeling totally inadequate for the promotion, and therefore finds one reason or another for turning it down. He may then be taken to task by his wife (perhaps because she intuitively senses that he is capable of taking on the job) and so the feelings of inadequacy increase with him. Similarly, someone enjoying a comfortable career, let's say an architect, suddenly finds himself faced with a calling from deep within himself to change to a career in medicine. This idea meets with considerable resistance from his family and friends, leading to one of two possible outcomes – either the energetic force for change is released through its fulfilment in a change of career, or the energetic force is suppressed.

Both these examples could result in illness because the thought processes would affect the mind, the mind might then transmit incorrect thought forms or vibrations into the physical body culminating in the possible development of physical illness at a pathological level in a very short time. The first example illustrates a thought or idea from an external source (in this case, a business superior) acting at a mind level which, if not responded to, can cause imbalance. The second example, in which a thought or idea manifests at an inner level (from the dimension of purpose within the individual himself), indicates how a conflict with our true path in life may have an influence on health and illness. Similar reactions to these may also occur at an emotional level – emotion being a response through love, hate, jealousy, anger, greed, desire, frustration, and so on. On the other hand, it is possible for a person to go through the whole of their life in total physical health, even though they occasionally transgress the laws of moderation regarding eating and drinking. In these cases, because the person is doing exactly what he or she feels comfortable with in life, they rarely fall ill.

Here lies the key to the role the individual themselves can play in maintaining harmonious health: by becoming aware of their inner tensions or conflicts through, so to speak, 'listening' to what their body, mind or emotions are telling them, they can overcome the tension or conflict by re-establishing the comfortable harmony that exists when their whole being is acting in accordance with their purpose. For some people, the path to self-awareness may be seen as lying in the hands of a personal guru, philosophical teacher or spiritual guide, and yet it is worth considering that while it may be desirable for us to learn from those more enlightened than ourselves, true self-awareness arises from within us at precisely the moment we are ready for it. In other words, the energy for additional awareness and healing lies within all of us.

In the modern Western world, with its emphasis on successfully attaining ever greater material or financial goals irrespective of whether or not this is in harmony with the individual's purpose in life, stress-related illnesses and disease abound. According to the traditional view, the cause of the stress is seen as arising from the person's job or environment whereas, viewed in a more holistic context, the stress may in fact stem from the conflict caused by the individual acting against his or her true path in life.

And yet it is not too difficult for us to see people enjoying mental and emotional harmony and leading satisfying lives. Take the elderly farm labourer, for example. He may be part of a now fast-disappearing breed, but he has spent his entire life working in the fields acquiring knowledge of the world of nature and its ways. He may even smoke and spend most of his evenings doing nothing more than sitting in his local pub, sipping the local ale or cider and playing dominoes. I have noticed that such people are frequently totally content with their lives. They may be relatively poor but they are free from the desire for further material gain. Their often quiet and unassuming manner comes from the mental and emotional harmony they experience, and from the comfortable enjoyment of the life they have chosen to lead. And how do such people usually look? Healthy!

I can't help comparing these old men (or their female equivalent) with the patients who come to me suffering from gastric ulcers or psoriasis, due not to bad dietary habits or smoking and drinking, but to overwork, stress and possibly the desire for improved social standing and material possessions that we refer to as 'keeping up with the Joneses'. In all such cases it is the thought processes of the patient that have caused an imbalance within the physical body. Why is this? Because incorrect thought processes, wrong reactions and erroneous attitudes will always manifest as an imbalance in the area of the physical body which has least resistance. This is not necessarily because of some inherited genetic fault; it is due to the fact that each of us has one or more areas of our body where the dimension of purpose expresses itself. Any suppression of this natural expression, or a thwarting of the intended path in life, will cause a depletion or over-reaction in that area.

How do we know that we human beings think or experience thought through areas of the body other than the brain? Take a bank manager, for example, who experiences continual work or environmental stress. If he is unable to cope with these factors, he may perhaps experience a duodenal ulcer, even though he has a loving wife who keeps him on a healthy diet and stands by him in all that he does. The stress and concern he is caused by the thoughts that continually worry him might manifest via the energy centre of the solar plexus in the physical body. In another person it could manifest through the head centre, causing incessant migraine headaches, and so on.

It would appear that the mental and emotional attitudes a person experiences during their lifetime respond to the inner sense of purpose by aligning themselves with, or sometimes diverging from, the path suggested by the thought forms that arise from within us. In this respect, it is perhaps easier for us to accept the laws governing the order of the universe and nature than it is to acknowledge that, much closer to home, we human beings are also subject to certain universal laws of order, and that illness and disease are little more than the effects of disharmony or lack of alignment and control relating to our purpose in life. It must also be remembered that people are not only influenced by their own free will, but also by the convictions of others around them, and that sometimes the two conflict.

This last statement should give much food for thought to those of us in the healing professions, for we really need to be in alignment within ourselves before attempting to heal others, or even endeavouring to give satisfactory counselling. We must also give serious thought to the possibility that thinking processes and thought exist in bodily dimensions other than the brain.

Much has been written and proven about right-brain mentation and the thinking processes that work away diligently at a sub-conscious level, controlling the autonomic nervous system and certain bodily functions without us becoming aware of them at a conscious level. This energizing by our built-in thought processes occurs as and when required, with thought patterns from the right-brain area causing corrective bodily actions to compensate for our continual environmental changes, as well as for the daily worries and stress we may experience.

As long as harmony and balance exist at a mind level, the energizing processes of purpose → mind → body can compensate completely for the changes that affect the physical body, doing it rapidly enough for the individual to remain healthy and yet not even be aware of the process taking place. Generally speaking, changes in depth of breathing, rate of pulse, release of blood sugar or healing of a minor flesh wound and so on all occur outside the normal range of our conscious awareness, indicating that it is essentially a subconscious activity directed by thought processes at a deeper level. However, even in a state of normal good health there are occasions when we become aware of some of these factors, but only when we are operating close to the limits of our physical tolerance – for example, the bouts of extreme tiredness that may affect us when driving our body to its near-maximum capabilities. Since we must assume that the innate thought processes governing the normal activity of a healthy body are in accordance with the purpose it was designed for, our awareness of these normally unconscious processes at a conscious level can be regarded as a sensible warning.

Such warnings can take the form of pain, tiredness, spasm or any one of the many other symptoms that we display to tell us that all is not as it should be within the deeper levels of organizing thought forms. Ignoring these warnings or symptoms can result in permanent organ damage and, of course, illness or disease. Moreover, if the emotional level also becomes involved because we cannot face making the necessary changes in our living habits or diet, or choose to resist making them, then further problems may arise. Very often we transgress the laws of nature in this way, attaching greater importance to our emotional needs than to our essential physical requirements. Ambition, greed and the desire to impress socially can lead us to adopt irregular eating and sleeping patterns, and to drink when it is socially appropriate rather than when our body genuinely requires liquid. In short, we override the innate thought processes that are there to govern the efficient functioning of our body.

A similar situation may occur when a patient seeks medical help for the physical symptoms that indicate a prompting by the vital essence for a change of attitude at an emotional or mental level. Where allopathic medicine is concerned, the patient will often be given drugs which negate the symptoms and yet, simultaneously, suppress the thoughts emanating from the patient's vital essence. This procedure converts the wonderful system of natural adjustment with which we are born, and which is part of our chosen path in life, into a system which becomes ever more stress-inducing as the natural energies come up against the barrier of suppressive drugs and negative incorrect thought forms. As a result of this, the inner thought processes may themselves generate inappropriate thoughts and communicate them to the body, thus causing further symptoms and stress.

Anyone who has ever consulted a medical dictionary, or one of the more widely available dictionaries of symptoms, will have been struck by the hundreds (if not thousands) of named diseases. In fact, these are really little more than lists of the labels which are given to clinically recognizable sets of symptoms and are generally not related to the basic causes. The latter are considerably fewer in number and can, I believe, be reduced to five principal classifications for the basic causes of disease:

1. So-called 'mechanical' injury to the body, and the resultant damage.
2. Detrimental substances in the body; an excess of toxins and/or poisons in the body and the results of auto-intoxication; the absence of substances needed by the body for growth, normal repair and maintenance.
3. Psychologically induced illness which may either be produced by the conflict between mental and emotional states, or by the patient's own self-induced conflict between their personality and the deeper self and the corresponding inability of the patient to come to terms with his or her real self.
4. What can loosely be called 'group contact'. This relates to the extent to which we are influenced by others and to what is frequently referred to as environmental stress (i.e. having to live and work in surroundings that place greater stresses on the individual than he or she was intended to bear).
5. Hereditary illness passed on genetically by one's parents and, perhaps, originating from less immediate ancestors. Those who subscribe to the reincarnation theory would include here the influences from the individual's own past lives.

Let's consider these five basic causes in a little more detail in the context of the central theme of this book.

Mechanical injury to the physical body includes not only the damage that occurs through accident but also the effects of, for example, the surgeon's scalpel and resultant scar tissue. (For reasons that will become apparent, incisions and scars can equally be placed under the heading of auto-intoxication.) When a scar passes through a meridian or energy channel, toxicity can travel from one area of the body to another. (See Chapter 3, 'Chinese philosophy' and 'The twenty-two subtle meridians'.) For example, many years after the successful removal of a tumour by surgery, a patient may possibly experience a secondary tumour in a totally different and remote part of the body from the primary tumour. It would appear that in some cases the reason for this is that scar tissue can have both toxicity and something called 'cell memory'. In our current example, the pattern or memory of the primary cause may lie in the cells around the area of the incision and these can then be passed on by the endergonic process to other parts of the body. (For an account of the endergonic process, see Chapter 1, p. 18.)

Deficiencies or excesses in the physical body initially arise from bad dietary habits and from the ingestion of allopathic drugs. A junk-food diet loaded with artificial colours, preservatives and a host of 'E' numbers will cause deficiencies or excesses that may affect the natural balance of the body's immune system and may, in turn, cause undesirable changes in the endocrine system in general – changes that the body will endeavour to correct at the level of its innate consciousness and which, if not dealt with successfully, can result in permanent damage.

Where psychologically induced illnesses are concerned, an emerging conflict between the variable thought processes of the mental and emotional states will create deficiencies or superfluities that affect the physical form. One may well ask how this is possible, but it is widely known and accepted that patients who suffer from continuous viral infections also often suffer from constant emotional stress. It is this stress, and the imbalance in thought processes that often accompanies it, which alters the wave forms that normally keep the dynamic balance of particles in harmony with the endocrine systems of the physical body. When the thymus gland, which is part of the endocrine system, is operating below par, the immune system is affected and invading viral infections therefore have a fertile soil on which to grow. On the other hand, those people who are harmoniously happy in both their human relationships and environment will rarely fall prey to such viruses. The causes of some cases of cancer comes from this category of psychologically induced illnesses. Why?

The twentieth-century Western system of measuring an individual's achievement and success in life by his or her material possessions and economic success (the cult of the so-called 'status symbol') has brought with it a whole new dimension of worry, stress and, in particular, a lack of emotional control when the individual is adversely affected by the greed of his or her own unreasonable desires for material gain. There is also an imbalance and disconnectedness in twentieth-century culture that is a contributory factor in the development of cancers. This cultural attitude is reflected in the fragmentary approach of medical research in considering the body as being simply the sum total of its parts, rather than as a whole. In following this approach, researchers have been led away from a true understanding of the causes of cancer, and from the discovery of a genuinely successful method for treating it.

The popular image of cancer promulgated by our divided culture and its communication media is that 'cancer' is synonymous with 'death'. Whatever the diagnosis, in treating the patient as an individual (whether for cancer or any other illnesses), some consideration should be given to the patient's case history and the emotional or psychological aspects this reveals. Was there any mental or emotional stress? Has the patient been isolated from their family, or lost someone they loved? Are they, for whatever reason, prone to feelings of guilt, and so on? Most patients are unfortunately so thoroughly conditioned in their views that they refuse even to consider the possible psychosomatic nature of their illness. On the contrary, cancer is often perceived and portrayed as a strong and powerful invader that attacks the body from the outside, with little hope of ever controlling it, let alone recovering from it to normal health. The nature of most current medical treatment for cancer – whether radiation, chemotherapy or surgery – tends to reinforce this perception because, for the most part, it is not only potentially drastic, traumatic and intrusive but, in the end, its effects are so often seen to be merely palliative.

Modern researchers now agree that not all cancer cells are the strong, powerful intruders they were once thought to be. For the most part they are simply cells which are weak and confused, and have run amok. The cancer cell does not actually attack and destroy – it simply overproduces. This overproduction arises from faulty information at a genetic level which is either due to the presence of harmful substances that the immune system cannot cope with or, as is more often the case, due to environmental influences. We need to remember that wave forms affect the particle formations, and so faulty information will prevent the cell from functioning normally. If a cell then reproduces others with the same incorrect genetic make-up, the end result is a mass of imperfect cells – in other words, a tumour. These imperfect cells are able to migrate to other parts of the body because the self-regulatory organization that normally occurs in cell communication and division is impaired. The migration may then set up more tumours in other areas of the body, but only if the immune system is totally depleted. A healthy immune system will recognize any abnormal cells and either destroy them or keep them isolated, thus preventing the spread of malignant cells.

One should therefore acknowledge that cancer is an attack from within the system and not an invasion from the outside world. Viewed from this perspective, the principal question that cancer researchers should be asking is: 'What is it that prevents a patient's immune system functioning normally at a particular time in his or her life, thus allowing certain cells to grow into a potentially life-threatening tumour?' The answer lies, I believe, in two directions of research.

The first of these is not to attribute the sole cause to certain carcinogenic substances but also to take into account the threatening situations that produce environmental stress. In cancer cases, it appears that the patient experiences a period of crucial stress at a point somewhere between three and eighteen months before the cancer is diagnosed. It also appears that prolonged stress channels incorrect mental attitudes and wave forms to a particular area of the body and cell functioning begins to break down. As far as the patient is concerned, serious illness and even death often seem to be the solution, not only at a conscious level but at a subconscious level as well, providing an escape from the overwhelming sense of inadequacy, despair or helplessness that the patient experiences in what is, to them, a totally hopeless situation. On the other hand, thoughts from within, and thus thoughts which are not necessarily expressed aloud, can have the most profound effects on the patient's ability to heal themselves, irrespective of the illness.

The second point to consider is the recognition of what it is *within* the individual patient that causes an illness, as well as the manner in which he or she reacts to it. The importance of the latter (the patient's own attitude to their situation) is generally overlooked. It is essential that they develop a tolerance and understanding of their situation, either when illness occurs (particularly where cancer is involved) or when their aims and ambitions collapse traumatically around them. Perhaps the concept that life's directives often come in the form of an illness is a difficult one to grasp fully. For instance, if a cancer is caused by an accumulation of unacknowledged frustration at a mental or emotional level, the illness gives the patient the opportunity to make a profound examination of themselves and perhaps acknowledge a situation they had previously ignored. In this sense, illness may be regarded as something like an initiation or gateway on our path through life, providing us with the possibility for a deeper understanding of ourselves and our fellow human beings.

The nature of our relationship and interaction with our fellow human beings brings us to the fourth basic cause of illness. Whilst the poisons and toxins that we ingest from our surroundings may affect us at a physical level, the contact with others and the *ambiance* or environment in which this contact takes place influence us at a mental and emotional level. The extent to which this influence affects us may vary, rather like the way in which ripples affect the still surface of a pond. It will perhaps be strongest where the immediate circle of our family and close friends is concerned and diminish as the closeness of our relationship to others diminishes. To refer again to the cancer patient, the reaction of his or her family and friends to the illness may have a positive or negative influence on the patient's own view of themselves, depending on whether the patient senses loving support or fear or confusion emanating from them.

In modern society, it is perhaps the fear of being left unloved and on our own that makes it so difficult for us to be truly 'whole' individuals, enjoying a harmonious balance between our sense of individuality and our personal relationships, and thus remaining relatively free from adverse influence by the strong convictions and emotions of others. One only needs to glance at the popular magazines to realize how much subtle pressure is brought to bear on us from outside ourselves with regard to our more intimate relationships. We may also experience from those close to us a more direct pressure to conform to certain conventional social patterns. The existence of adverse outside pressures of this kind, particularly where relationships with an intimate partner are concerned, can inhibit true individuality. Here again, we encounter the fine nature of the balance between developing as an individual according to our own goals in life and being in harmony with our fellow human beings. In our dealings with others we need to realize that it is possible to be 'ourselves' and tolerate each other's differences without this detracting from genuinely gratifying and fulfilling relationships.

Many patients who consult me have a causative factor in their illness stemming from some inadequacy or another experienced in their relationship with their partner. Perhaps they tell me of a career change, sometimes involving a change of surroundings as well, that they would like to make and yet dare not mention this to their partner or other members of their family, for fear of disapproval or scorn. The lack of individual strength thus manifested can cause a lack of both physical resonance and resistance to infection. When situations like this occur we need to react positively, just as we need to react positively to any illness that befalls us, not negatively accepting it as simply being part of what 'fate' has in store for us.

Our adoption of a positive attitude when faced with an illness or an apparently negative situation is also of more benefit to us therapeutically than a simple turning away or avoidance of it. When patients face their illness positively and squarely the energy thus generated by their experience accounts for many of the otherwise inexplicable spontaneous remissions or miraculous healings.

Lastly, the fifth basic cause of illness is that attributable to genetic inheritance and passed on to us by our parents, or perhaps emanating from even further back in our ancestral line. Illnesses originating from this cause appear to be unavoidable, as do the physical weaknesses and susceptibilities to certain illnesses with which we may come into this world. In common with the four other causes, illnesses of this kind can be understood as an opportunity for the patient either to respond positively to a given situation or to meekly accept it as a part of their so-called 'fate'. When I tell patients that they have, so to speak, 'chosen' their own illness I understandably get mixed reactions. And yet, if we acknowledge that at a superficial level of consciousness we choose a particular career or path in life, we should be able to accept that the same is also true of our deeper levels of consciousness. In other words, at a deeply subconscious level of the mind, we choose our own life experiences and deeper aspirations as part of our continuing education and evolution. It is how we react to these experiences that has a bearing on our health and on our progress along our evolutionary path, and a positive reaction ensures continuing health.

In order for the healing process to be truly effective we need to be aware of a proper sense of purpose to our lives, for without a sense of purpose there can be no evolution (conscious or otherwise), and no lasting restoration of health. When we ourselves may be suffering from a severe or chronic illness, or even a degenerative disease, it perhaps sounds all too easy to be reminded that there *is* a purpose to life, and that the purpose knows what its purpose is. The difficult part is for us to become aware of our own purpose, and work towards fulfilling it within the universal order of things. (See Chapter 3, 'Tibetan philosophy'.)

THE DIAGNOSIS

It is important for any practitioner to remember that the patient is not just *another* patient. They are an individual human being and should thus, at the very least, be given the respect and courtesy that we ourselves would expect in a similar situation. The establishment of a good rapport based on mutual trust between the patient and the person who is treating them can sometimes, of itself, make a significant contribution in the initial steps on the road to recovery. Conversely, if this essential rapport is lacking, the patient may possibly be discouraged, thus finding the initial steps more difficult to make.

When proceeding with the patient's diagnosis, it is essential for any practitioner to draw up a comprehensive case history of the individual patient. Unlike his allopathic colleague, the practitioner of natural medicine regards observable symptoms in the physical body as being less important than other factors which may be revealed by the patient's case history. In building up a picture of the patient, questions which appear quite straightforward may, in the overall context, reveal subtle details about the patient's background and possible causes of stress, trauma or contact with environmental pollutants.

Each practitioner will have his or her own sequence of preferred questions which may include initial enquiries regarding the patient's place of birth, schooling, further education and choice of career. Did the patient grow up in a rural or urban area? Was the patient's family close-knit, with both parents living together in the home, or was one or other of the parents often absent, perhaps even leading a separate life due to the breakdown of the marriage? Did the patient attend boarding school and, if so, was it voluntarily or involuntarily? What are their recreational or other interests? Adult patients would be asked about their marital status.

All these questions help to build up a picture of the patient's background and, of course, in asking them the practitioner should employ as sympathetic a manner as possible. As well as listening to the patient's answers, the practitioner will also note the manner of their response to the questions. For example, are they happy or reluctant to answer certain questions? If a particular question appears to strike the patient as intrusive, why is this so? Does their sensitivity to it stem from the lack of confidence or a weak sense of identity, or does it touch on an area that has caused the patient suffering in the past (physical, mental or emotional, or perhaps even a combination of all of these), from which they still bear the scars?

So far none of the questions have been about the patient's symptoms. This is intentional for the symptoms may be regarded as an end product, and the primary aim is to establish their underlying cause. In asking the patient about their health the practitioner needs to establish as full a picture as possible. This may mean asking about the types of illness they have suffered from in the past, even as a child, and whether or not there is a history of any particular illness within their family. When it comes to discussing the patient's recent medical history, the practitioner will ask about any course of treatment or therapy they have undergone, what drugs were used, and to what effect. If they have been consulting a complementary practitioner, have they also had an orthodox diagnosis – and if so, what did this reveal?

In the course of my own consultations with patients, I ask

them how they view their own temperament, how they react in different social circumstances, and in their own immediate environment – in other words, how do they see themselves? I also ask them about their personal habits such as smoking, alcohol consumption, excessive tea or coffee drinking, and also their eating habits and dietary tendencies (for instance, do they follow a general diet, or are they a vegetarian or vegan?).

The consultation procedure may involve gently drawing the patient's attention to any contradictions they may make; not in order to correct them but simply to resolve any underlying confusion or ascertain its source. In one sense, the consultation is a 'drawing out' process, in the course of which the patient (particularly if they are mentally alert or sensitive) may themselves learn a great deal. It may even be the first time in many years that they have sat down and talked openly about themselves, their lives, their hopes, fears, ambitions and their illness.

All of the above falls into its natural place when viewed in conjunction with the patient's current physical, emotional or mental symptoms along with the interpretation of their blueprint formula. By way of a contrast, the more traditional orthodox approach to the diagnostic process is to establish the name of the disease that fits the accumulated physical symptoms displayed by the patient. This approach entails the examination or observation of the visible symptoms, aided when necessary by a variety of instruments or techniques – X-rays, screenings, scans, blood tests, and so on – some of which can be painful and invasive. If no conclusions can readily be drawn from these investigations, the doctor may refer the patient to a specialist, or to a surgeon for further exploration within the body.

The anomaly of treating the symptoms rather than the cause really came home to me some years ago when I attended a seminar on the subject of incontinence. Five or six eminent doctors and researchers in the field delivered excellent papers on the condition, and there were also some twenty or more exhibition stands devoted to the drugs, equipment, catheters and protective clothing then used in its treatment. It struck me, however, that the dominant focus of attention in all this was ultimately the *effect*, not the *cause*, and yet, in all illness, there is an underlying equation of cause = effect. I found myself asking the question, why, in the midst of all this marvellous demonstration of the knowledge, research and equipment available on the subject, was no one addressing the actual *cause* of illness in the patient? Failing to find a genuinely satisfactory answer, I could only conclude (possibly somewhat cynically) that the economic factor played an over-important role in medicine – namely, when a patient is cured the medical 'industry' as a whole suffers because there are no return visits to the doctors and specialists, and thus no repeat orders for drugs, equipment or associated merchandise. In other words, I was struck by the apparent contradiction of a medicine whose professed aim was to restore the patient to 'normal' health and yet which concentrated its attention on the treatment and cure of localized symptoms.

Another factor that confuses the picture placed before the doctor, especially in the light of a training which regards the human body as little more than a very complex machine, is that orthodox medicine persists in producing *one* basic type of drug for a particular illness. The drug is then used to treat all the many different individuals who display the same recognizable set of symptoms. And yet, when we consider the nature of human individuality and the extent to which, in normal everyday life, we regard the individual (with his or her thoughts, emotions and idiosyncratic habits) as being so much more than a mere physical body, it becomes increasingly evident that to treat the real cause of illness one needs to treat the individual as a whole. We can illustrate this last point briefly with the hypothetical case of a patient experiencing continual viral infections. On the one hand, the patient can be treated for the symptoms of each infection as and when it occurs; on the other, we can consider the possibility that in order to host this succession of viruses, the threshold of the patient's immune system must already have been lowered by another factor, other than the virus itself. In other words, the cause of the symptoms in the physical body may well lie at a level *beyond* the physical.

A further factor that possibly clouds the diagnostic capabilities of orthodox medicine is that, to date, little attention has been paid to the relevance of quantum physics for human biology within the context of conventional diagnostic procedures. For example, if an epinephrine molecule can be produced by a thought (the thought of fear), what molecules, hormones and other biochemical changes take place while the patient is sitting anxiously in a hospital waiting room, sometimes for a very long period of time, busily thinking about what might or might not be wrong with them? The answer has to be: secretions and changes in normal bodily function that might possibly cloud the diagnosis. It is also worth considering the tissue or other material that is removed from the body in the course of a biopsy for later examination. This material, often examined many hours or even days later, is no longer influenced by the total electromagnetic force field of the body from which it was taken. More importantly, it has been separated from its purpose. In our present equation of *purpose* = mind = body, the removal of any one element from the equation will impair the chances of finding a completely satisfactory answer regarding the cause of the patient's illness.

In Chapter 3 we spoke of the EPR experiment (see p. 73) and the influence of the observer upon the observed. It was noted that not only can the non-local effects upon the observed be measured but that they can also be influenced by the mind of the observer. When we apply this phenomenon to the testing of blood samples, can we be absolutely sure that there is no influence exerted upon the outcome of the laboratory test by the mind of the observer? I don't think so. In fact, I often wonder how much the samples of blood and tissue removed from patients, sometimes to a distant laboratory, will come under the influence of an observer testing for certain anomalies. Can the thought of these anomalies in the observer's mind cause them to manifest, albeit at an energetic level? We must further consider the possibility of 'action at a distance' and non-local effects upon the patient during the testing process, even though the patient may be far away. Similarly, we should consider the effect of the impact on the patient's mind when the findings are given to them in the form of a verbal or written report, as well as the thoughts occurring in the mind of the patient while they are waiting, perhaps with some anxiety, to receive it.

The above are perhaps some of the reasons why many of the patients who consult me and other practitioners of natural medicine tell the same story. Either the doctor had told them that they could find nothing wrong with them, or, because no cause could be found for the symptoms, no more could be done for them.

In spite of the apparently negative nature of some of these

comments, I am also well aware of the very important contribution that scientific medicine has made to advances in health
care. Many thousands of patients have benefited from orthodox
examinations and modern technology, but imagine what further
advances could be made to those patients floundering by the
wayside if medicine would accept a new biomedical model of
humanity to replace the outdated mechanical one. When this
does happen, the use of impersonal equipment such as scanners
and X-rays in conjunction with a personal diagnosis that takes
into account the three dimensions – purpose, mind and body –
of the whole individual would forge a closer and more active
two-way bond between the patient and his or her practitioner.

PATIENT PARTICIPATION

It may seem a very obvious thing to say but the primary need
for the patient in any healing process is the intention to get
well. This intention does not confine itself to mere cooperation
with the doctor or practitioner; it has to be an intention, at the
most profound level, for the patient to *want* to get well and to
participate willingly and wholeheartedly in their own healing
process.

The exact nature of the patient's participatory role is variable.
It may take the form of oral medication, dietary changes, taking
more exercise, establishing a daily routine, cutting down on
cigarettes or alcohol, and so on. One practitioner I know gives
his patients a role by setting them a form of 'home-work'. At
the end of the initial consultation, he writes out a list of 'do's
and don'ts' for each patient and, in addition, gives them a
programme of participation in their own healing process. At
the second appointment, the patient is questioned regarding the
progress they have made. If they have not tackled the home-
work, the practitioner simply says, 'Come back and see me next
month, when you have completed your home-work'.

Healing is cooperation: the practitioner makes the suggestions
and it is up to the patient to carry them out. Nothing is ever
achieved by the patient merely placing themselves in the hands
of the doctor and saying, 'Here I am, Doc, do me a favour and
fix me up. I know I can leave it all up to you, 'cause that's
your job, isn't it?' The patient *must* participate in his or her

own healing, and yet the waiting room of the average general practice seems to be full of patients who expect the doctor to do all the work for them – perhaps, in some instances, even wishing that they would actually pick up the prescription from the chemist and take the medication for them as well.

Fortunately, this near-traditional attitude is gradually changing, but how did it arise in the first place? Is it because of the patient's detachment from their own healing process? Does this detachment originate in an inordinate fear of illness and disease, and so the greater the distance between us and our illness the better? Or does it come from the patient's own perception of the doctor as an all-powerful and distant being with near-miraculous powers? Is it due to the conventional medical concept of the physical body as little more than a mechanical object? Whatever the reason, the greater the gulf between the patient and their illness or between themselves and the person treating them, the less likely it is that the patient will be healed.

In this respect, it must also be said that there are 'good' doctors and practitioners and there are 'bad' ones. I sometimes wonder how many patients feel that the person they have entrusted themselves to is not the 'right' person for them, either because they seem impersonal and unsympathetic, or because, for one reason or another, the patient simply senses intuitively that things are not as they need to be, and yet they continue to go to them for treatment. Perhaps the patient is afraid of causing offence by changing to another doctor or practitioner, or else they feel they have no 'right' to do so.

All these factors will influence the healing process because they affect the extent of the patient's active participation in it. Why should this active participation be so important? The short answer is that the patient, consciously or unconsciously, participated actively in the origin and development of their own illness. When seen from the perspective of natural medicine, this means that the patient chose to expose themselves to a particular situation and to react to the resulting stresses or traumas in a certain way. In other words, they exercised a degree of free will in making their choice. These choices are influenced by the same elements that affect all the choices and decisions we make in our lives, such as our personality and external environment, as well as social and cultural attitudes.

Whether it is seen to act at an unconscious or conscious level, the part played by the patient's free will is an important element to take into consideration. I recall one particular case that happened some years ago. A woman I had successfully treated for migraine a few months previously telephoned to say that she was sending her husband along to me for a consultation. When the husband arrived, almost the first thing he said was something like, 'My wife says that you've got to fix my sciatica'. It was fairly clear from the outset that he had no real intention that I should 'fix his sciatica'. From the answers he gave to my questions, it became obvious that a cure would mean he no longer had an excuse to avoid doing mundane things like helping with the washing up or working in the garden when his wife asked him to do so. In other words, his illness was a 'crutch' he had chosen to help him shun certain situations.

Further questions revealed that this choice had been made of his own free will, at the level of his personality, so that he could do the things he wanted to do and escape from the shared responsibilities of the family circle. The counselling I endeavoured to give this patient had little or no effect and, in the end, I told him quite bluntly that there was no real point in us going any further, nor in him going to any other therapist to get his sciatica 'fixed', unless he first changed his attitude. Understandably, he disagreed with my diagnosis and interpretation of the underlying cause of his illness and he left, saying that he preferred the orthodox type of treatment and insisting that the painkillers were working, even though his doctor had not found the cause of the problem. In cases such as this, the patient cannot expect a change for the better unless they themselves change their attitude, developing not only the will to take responsibility for their own health but also the will to accept the responsibilities, however mundane these may appear to be, that occur in their relationships with others.

The *will to live* functions continually throughout our lives and the power of this will, manifesting in the patient as the will to get well, is crucial for the success of the healing process. Of equal importance is the patient's confidence in the doctor or practitioner and the type of treatment involved. Any negative resonances here will bring disharmony and obstruct the efficacy of the course of treatment. One of the most testing moments for this relationship is when the doctor tells the patient their illness is such that they have at most only six or nine months to live. Statements of this kind have a powerful impact on the mind–body system, acting like a shock wave at a subconscious level.

Patients with a diagnosed terminal illness should be given an ongoing long-term goal, not just one of a few months. Sometimes the patient sets his or her own long-term goal. For example, a cancer patient who is told that their illness is terminal and they have under a year to live may respond by saying that this can't be so; it's imperative that they see their little boy or girl into primary school, and that's in two years' time. The patient's determination to fulfil this goal is so great that they live just long enough to see it through, but no longer, for no further goal was set. The incentive for life must be continually progressive, and not restricted to a finite number of months. Having said that, it must also be said that on some rare occasions, the violent shock of being told they only have a few months left re-awakens the power of the patient's will to live to such a degree that they recover totally in a matter of weeks.

The healing power of thought emanating from the patient's mind has frequently been proved by the 'placebo effect'. The use of a placebo is not restricted to taking dummy pills, but plays a significant role in many types of therapy where it is employed intentionally to produce its effect, and not merely to humour the patient. Unfortunately, like the term 'psychosomatic', 'placebo' has a derogatory connotation that tends to belittle the power of the mind rather than acknowledge its potential role in the healing process. In a similar way, the rather vague expression 'spontaneous remission' is commonly used in conventional medical practice to explain the unexpected disappearance of a patient's symptoms but, in real terms, this is no explanation at all. Perhaps it is more the unwitting recognition of the point at which the traditional 'mechanical' approach to medicine finally runs out of explanations, but is not yet honest or brave enough to admit its own shortcomings.

My overall view of healing has always been that it represents a progressive stage in the patient's own evolution, and not simply remedial treatment at a physical level. When the patient first approaches the doctor or practitioner, apparently with the wish to be healed, they are in fact expressing an initial desire to progress to the next stage of their evolutionary path. It is therefore important not only for the motivation provided by this desire to be kept alive, but also for the patient to understand the deeper reasons for his or her ill health. During the consultation process, I will communicate to the patient only that information which I consider to relate to the causal factor of his or her illness, providing them at the same time with a course of treatment which will continue to motivate their intention to progress along their path in life.

The actual form of this treatment will vary from one patient to the next, but in the healing process I believe it is important to give advice or administer some kind of remedy on a daily, weekly or even monthly basis. The actual taking of the remedy can work at the level of the mind as well as at a physical/biochemical level, for the cycle of remedy-taking reminds the patient of the link and mutual commitment of both parties to their progress. Each time the remedy is swallowed the patient experiences, perhaps only at a subconscious level, some of the rapport that took place during the consultation. At the same time it is to be hoped that they feel they are taking another step along the road to recovering normal health.

It may be possible to relieve the patient's symptoms in the short term, but unless the cause of the symptoms is found they will simply appear elsewhere, perhaps on a different physical or mental level. The cause is often hidden, perhaps lying rooted in thwarted goals or the lack of fulfilment of one's aims and ambitions, or in the particular career one has chosen to follow, thus blocking the natural evolutionary flow of life. In this sense life is very much like the flow of a river towards the sea. If the estuary becomes blocked, the water backs up until it forces a breach in the banks or finds another route to the sea. If in turn this too becomes blocked, then the process will occur again – and again and again, for the goal of the river is to flow uninterrupted to the sea. The cause of symptoms is similar to the blockage in the flow of the river, while the symptoms themselves are comparable to the breaches that appear in the river banks. If the symptoms are merely covered over with a palliative drug, the blocked energy (which is perhaps a blocked or suppressed emotion, aim, ambition or similar goal) will appear in another part of the body.

THE POWER OF THOUGHT FORMS

The power of thought processes and the act of thinking, and their effect upon the human organism in connection with health and illness, have largely been ignored by the conventional approach to modern medicine. The term 'mind–body' medicine is employed by many natural practitioners to convey the important role of thought not only in the healing process, but also as a causative factor acting at very profound levels of our conscious and subconscious minds.

When counselling patients, I often suggest that if they concentrate on the end requirement or goal they wish to attain, the thought that will enable them to fulfil their goal will arise naturally and at the appropriate time to be put into action. On the other hand, if they focus the energy of their thoughts on worrying about how they will achieve their goal, the flow of thought between themselves and their goal is interrupted and its powerful energy is diverted into generating yet more worry.

In an earlier chapter we mentioned that energy follows thought and that a thought always precedes an action, whether this is related to an action of the physical body or the construction of an inanimate object. The productive power of thought is the greatest creative force within the universe and precedes the material manifestation of all things. We acknowledge this to some extent in our use of the expression 'mind over matter'. In fact, the very act of thinking itself has repercussions in the physical body, for it can cause changes in the blood supply, blood pressure and pulse rate. After a period of protracted mental concentration, the body becomes sluggish and tired, making it more difficult for the mind to continue working efficiently – a phenomenon we have probably all experienced at one time or another.

Thought can and should be a constructive agent, but it can also be destructive in relation to the health of the individual. Good health is obviously more enjoyable than ill health; even so, there are those who seem to 'enjoy' the latter. Perhaps their pleasure is derived not so much from the actual illness, but more from the constant attention they receive through being ill.

There are many different terms used to express the power of thought in relation to illness – psychosomatic, self-limiting, hysterical, and so on – each of which is capable of producing symptoms at a pathological level. However, probably the most powerful aspect of thought as a major cause of illness is fear, for it can weaken the body and lower the threshold of the immune system. The recognition of fear-induced illness is nothing new. Some years ago in Africa I heard an ancient Arab tale in which Pestilence met a caravan on the desert road to Baghdad.

'Why are you going to Baghdad?', asked the Arab in charge of the caravan.

'To take five thousand lives,' replied Pestilence.

On the way back from the city the paths of Pestilence and the caravan crossed once more.

'You told me a lie,' protested the Arab angrily to Pestilence. 'Instead of five thousand lives you took fifty thousand.'

'That is untrue,' replied Pestilence. 'I told you no lie. I said I would take five thousand lives and that is all I took, not one more or less. It was fear that killed the rest.'

Of course, organic disease can be attributed to factors other than thought, but the crucial role played by thought in the process of maintaining health or developing ill health is too great to be ignored. Sometimes illnesses and ailments can be of an entirely imaginary nature – not that the symptoms are imaginary; they are real enough, arising from an underlying emotional or mental cause. In such cases it is useless to treat just the symptoms. That would be rather like giving morphine to a man with a broken leg in the hope that, by removing the pain, the leg will heal. The injury itself must be effectively treated before the pain goes away, for the injury is itself the cause of the pain.

Generally speaking, although thought is most readily associated with the production and cure of physiological diseases, there are other areas, equally real and painful for the sufferer, in which it operates. There is, for example, the thought of inferiority, commonly referred to as the 'inferiority complex'. This complex can arise from one or more of a number of causes: a physical deformity which excludes the sufferer from aspects of normal day-to-day activity; a prominent scar, facial or other physical feature of which a sensitive person is always conscious and therefore chooses to hide themselves, in one way or another, from the gaze of others; a sense of built-up frustration through not finding an outlet for nervous energy; failure of one kind or another, resulting in the conviction of incompetence or ineptitude; unkind teasing or destructive criticism, especially as a child. All of these frequently result in the sufferer developing a disorder of some kind, with or without pathological symptoms, so that he or she may find some compensation in the sympathy of others and solace in becoming the centre of attraction and attention. The sufferer is probably blissfully unaware of what he or she is doing, and of the motive which prompts them to develop their particular pattern of behaviour.

An inferiority complex can emanate from a group of ideas within the individual, but there is usually one central theme: the lack of belief in oneself, although this may be further defined as the feeling that one lacks any value in the community, or is lacking any ability in this or that direction. Sometimes the centre of the complex also includes thoughts of fear and helplessness, and the negative nature of these thoughts can be very destructive where the physical organism is concerned. When these thoughts take hold at a mental or emotional level, the sufferer may manifest a dislike of meeting other people, or a fear of strangers. They may even develop the tendency to hide themselves completely away from their fellow human beings, so confusing and intolerable do they find the close proximity of others.

In the end, this avoidance of others can become an obsession; that is, the thought of avoiding contact with other people dominates the mind to such an extent that avoidance becomes the motivating force, to the exclusion of all other thoughts and ideas. The obsession can induce ill health because the person is increasingly incapable of leading a normally active life. Many obsessions are relatively mild and harmless, but others are of such a persistent nature that they can upset mental stability, even to the point of being a danger to the sanity of the sufferer. A fairly common obsession is the continual washing of hands and the overwhelming desire for pristine cleanliness of oneself and one's household. This over-concern for purity is often found when the person is plagued by guilt or remorse at a subconscious level. Perhaps they secretly practise a habit regarded (in their eyes, at least) as socially or morally unacceptable, or have at some time in the past suffered abuse at the hands of another. The personality reacts to their inner feeling of being unclean in a symbolic manner by adopting an overconscientious and exaggerated external cleanliness.

The examples given so far – fear, inferiority complexes, obsessions – are all attitudes of mind and are therefore controlled by thought, even when a physical experience has occasioned them or they are expressed in physical terms. Emotion and instinct are both strong and their influence cannot be disregarded but, since human beings also benefit from the gift of rational thought, they need not be enslaved by them.

Patients who are helped to change their thought processes either by counselling or by taking some form of natural energetic medicine find that their fears and apprehensions can be overcome. The dangers by which they imagine themselves to be surrounded will take on a less terrifying aspect and they will become increasingly tolerant of the various factors that previously disturbed them. For instance, the thoughts of inadequacy harboured by a patient suffering from an inferiority complex, however they may have originated, hamper the innate process of self-healing. As the change of mental attitude is nurtured by careful counselling or gentle remedies and the patient actively participates in his or her own healing process by consciously working to adopt a different mental approach to life, the complex will gradually disappear. The patient will no longer seek an escape, or desire an unnatural outlet for pent-up energies. The same applies to the patient suffering from an obsession. If, with the help of counselling, he or she can be helped to expand the single focus of their mental attention, they will gradually be able to see things from a more realistic perspective and in their right relationship to other thoughts and ideas, thus ridding themselves of their obsession and achieving a generally more balanced outlook on life.

A qualified psychotherapist or experienced counsellor is essential for patients suffering from such complexes and obsessions. It is also important for the patient to understand that his or her condition can ultimately be cured, especially if they train themselves to use positive thinking to counteract the causative thoughts or negative ideas, for the suffering itself is intensified or relieved according to the patient's own mental attitude.

The condition of our mind also affects the extent to which we feel physical pain. By concentrating our thoughts, it is possible to increase or diminish its intensity. If our mind is occupied with thoughts other than of the pain (sometimes a difficult thing to achieve because pain can be so demanding of our attention), we can endure intense suffering bravely, for when the pain is no longer at the forefront of our consciousness we are, in effect, unconscious of it. I have seen my children fall over or injure a knee and yet, because the enjoyment or excitement of the game was at the forefront of their mind, they have continued playing. Once the game was over, however, it was a different story. The pain or injury moved in to occupy the space left vacant in the conscious mind by the termination of the game.

In times of illness, it is often difficult for us to remember that we are blessed by the healing power of nature, the healing power of the vital essence within us all, but it is thought that motivates and supplies the power to the healing process. By correct thinking we may overcome disease and assist recovery, and by the power of thought we may mitigate pain, and even lengthen life. We would be wise to acknowledge and remember the incalculable effect of thought upon the body of the thinker. But what about the effect of the thoughts of others upon us? What about the thoughts of the practitioner when he or she is endeavouring to assist the patient in the healing process?

Having considered the effect of our own thought processes upon our physical body, we must also bear in mind the fact that one person's thoughts can affect the thoughts of another. No one seems to know quite how telepathy works, nor the particular conditions required for it to work, although it is generally accepted that a sympathetic affinity is a recurring factor in most documented cases. Perhaps the transference of thought becomes easier to understand if we recall the twin phenomena of 'action at a distance' and non-localized effects occurring in the interaction between the observer and the observed (see p. 73), as well as the idea that 'energy follows thought'. In other words, as well as thoughts and ideas being transmitted from one person to another through the medium of speech, they can also be transmitted, consciously or unconsciously, at the level of thought itself. However, thoughts and ideas can only be implanted in another mind if the second mind is open to receive them. And they will only be translated into action (or further thought), if the second mind accepts them as its own.

The transmission and acceptance of thought between two minds has the power to influence health, as I witnessed in Africa where the witch-doctor uses thought in this way to perform acts of healing. Of course, nothing can take effect unless the patient believes in, and accepts, the witch-doctor's power to perform these acts. And then, only when there is a belief or faith in the idea or thought will it be admitted into the consciousness of the individual to manifest via the mind into the physical body.

Irrespective of the therapy practised, healing can only take place at the level of thought when the patient has in their mind, at a conscious or subconscious level, the intention of cooperating with the practitioner and, of course, the intention to be healed as well. Furthermore, the healing of chronic illness, even at a pathological level, often takes place initially at a very profound level of the mind, with the use of energetic or antimatter remedies serving to trigger the missing thought or vibration in order for the vital essence of the patient to heal at a physical dimension.

Although we can't see them or handle them, it is obvious to us that thoughts exist. It is also obvious that thoughts and ideas entering the mind come from somewhere but, if it is not we who create our thoughts, where do they come from? Like many others who work in the fields of natural medicine and healing, I believe that thoughts exist before we become aware of them, and they persist even when we are no longer cognizant of them. In other words, they exist before and after we acknowledge them as being *our* thoughts. Thoughts are universal in origin, existing 'out there' in the universal order of things. All we do as mere human beings is tune into them by tuning the wavelength of our mind – our own 'thought receiver' – to the wavelength of thought we require, rather like tuning in a radio to receive the broadcast from a particular radio station transmitting on a given wavelength. After all, what is thought other than a wave form or vibration? Perhaps it is not measurable in physical terms, but its behaviour conforms to the wave/particle theory of quantum physics (see p. 71).

In everyday life each of us has our own particular wavelength or resonance of thought, just as we have our own unique set of fingerprints. This individual resonance of thought vibration allows us to draw in the thought processes we require for daily living and our evolutionary path in life, as well as the thought processes that govern our bodily functions. When the physical body becomes sick, our innate intelligence or vital essence tunes to the wavelength or vibration needed to correct the imbalance. However, if the reception of the required incoming thoughts is jammed by interference emanating from our own mental or emotional vibration, then the symptoms that occur are nothing more than an indication of the blocked thought process. The reception of the appropriate thought processes can be helped by the ingestion of natural energetic remedies to bring about the correct wave form vibration necessary for the healing process to take place.

Energetic remedies of this kind themselves contain the required vibration or wavelength of thought which, coming directly from the world of nature, is free of the interference transmitted by our own mental or emotional state. In other words, to return to our analogy of the radio station, when there is a malfunction in our receiver, making it too weak to tune in to the signal we need to receive, the energetic remedy provides us with a powerful signal-booster. Not only does this enable us to receive the required transmission, but the newly strengthened signal brings about the repair of the cause of the malfunction.

In examining the power of thought and the different levels at which this power can function, reference has been made several times to the rational and intuitive minds. Perhaps a further word of explanation is necessary, especially in the context of the mutual participation of the patient and practitioner in the healing process. Biologically speaking, our physical brain consists of two hemispheres – left and right. The left brain is the seat of our rational mind (the logical and discriminative thinking processes) whilst the right brain is the seat of our intuitive mind or, as some might call it, the area of extrasensory perception, where the thoughts from the universal mind pour in. We might also say that they correspond respectively to levels of consciousness: the one is our relatively shallow day-to-day consciousness which deals with what it finds immediately before it; the other is our subconsciousness (or deeper levels of consciousness) which, through its link with the universal mind, is, in theory, bottomless. Being two halves of the same brain or mind, they should function together in harmonious union, but all too often the clatter of our shallower thought processes drowns the messages being communicated from our intuition (or inner voice), causing us to think and act independently of our true purpose in life. Ultimately, it is this lack of harmony that manifests itself as a disorder of one kind or another at a physical level, unless the thought processes are retuned to their correct wave vibration.

The knowledge that thought, and thought alone, can keep a person in good health or cause disease is something that should be borne in mind by every doctor, practitioner and patient but, in the final analysis, our understanding of the cause of illness is related to the cause of life itself. In reality, the latter is not created and directed by governmental institutions or economic policies any more than ill health is caused by physical symptoms. These are but the external and tangible expressions of the underlying and unseen power of thought. Our understanding of this external and tangible world is vast compared to that of the world of thought from which it emanates. Perhaps we should acknowledge that our knowledge of the latter is still in its infancy and that, as we too are but an emanation of thought from the universal mind, so is our knowledge of ourselves.

CHAPTER 5

Matter and Antimatter Remedies

It has long been accepted that no two individuals share the same fingerprints and it is now also becoming more widely acknowledged that constitution, strength and weaknesses similarly differ from one individual to the next. The recognition of this fact has resulted in a questioning of whether the practice of using similar remedies for different patients displaying similar symptoms is really the optimum form of treatment it was once claimed to be. If the approach to healing is to be changed, and turned literally inside-out, working from the formative level within the subtle realms of causation towards the manifestation of the physical form (rather than from the outside in, where the physical symptoms are generally dealt with first), we must also consider using a range of remedies that extends from the drugs of orthodox medical practice to the non-material remedies of quantum electrodynamics.

Whether the remedy chosen to treat the patient is 'orthodox' or 'complementary' in origin, it should be chosen according to the vital essence of each individual. The reason for this is that the symptoms of disease will only manifest when the blueprint of life is not adhered to. For healing to be effective, the treatment must strengthen and restore the vital essence.

Every remedy, from a material drug to the antimatter remedies of homoeopathic medicine, possesses a wave/particle duality and therefore, by aligning the remedy to the appropriate area of the formative blueprint, the cells and organ systems will themselves become realigned through the action of correct thought form.

MATERIAL REMEDIES: DRUGS AND HERBS

As we mentioned in an earlier chapter, the Chinese started practising herbalism some 5000 years ago. Until fairly recent times, it was also widely practised in the Western world. Today, however, virtually all the drugs in current use in Western medicine have been developed in the laboratory and are manufactured by various chemical processes. Many modern drugs are synthetic forms of naturally occurring substances although, according to the claims of the drug companies who make them and the orthodox practitioners who prescribe them, these chemical copies are indistinguishable from the originals. Some drugs are still obtained from plants – for example, Belladonna (deadly nightshade) which is used for some gastro-intestinal disorders, or the opiate drugs (including morphine) which are derived from the poppy – while certain vaccines and hormone treatments are obtained from animal sources. The majority of drug companies now appear to favour laboratory-produced drugs, most of which are the result of genetic engineering – a process by which the genes (which direct cell function) of certain micro-organisms are altered, thus changing the end-product of a cell's activity.

An example of the above practice is insulin, a hormone produced in the pancreas, which is essential in controlling the level of glucose in the bloodstream. As a drug, it is invaluable in the treatment of diabetes and, although at one time it was obtained from the pancreatic glands of cattle and pigs, it can now be manufactured by genetically engineered 'bacteria'. This, and other dramatic advances by genetic engineers in the search to produce remedies, leads one to question why there have not been similar advances in the treatment of the pancreas which is itself responsible for the condition. To what extent has the direction of research been influenced by the potentially vast revenues at stake for the drug companies from the sale of their remedies? Or, to put the same question another way, how much has research been influenced by the potentially huge losses in revenue to the drug companies from the drop in sales of insulin, should the cause of the malfunction in the pancreas be cured?

In its treatment of patients, orthodox medicine addresses the relief of the symptoms rather than the actual causation of the patient's illness. There is no doubt, however, that allopathic drugs do produce spectacular cures where some patients are concerned but, at the same time, this effect is purely palliative for other patients suffering from the same illness. If orthodox medicine were to consider a different approach, one that could pinpoint the cause of illness, the use of a drug related to that cause would result in a greater success rate of permanent cures. In instances where patients have experienced dramatic cures and returned to optimum health after taking allopathic drugs, it is obvious that the drug was actually healing the cause of the condition. To take this point further, it is evident that the drug acted as a catalyst within the blueprint or vital essence of the patient.

Other patients who experience purely palliative effects from a drug, but no cure, often develop further symptoms or side effects. This would indicate that, far from serving as the catalyst for change required by the patient's vital essence, the particular drug being used is having the opposite effect. If we consider a diuretic drug, for example, which is used to get rid of excess body water in patients suffering from obesity or blood pressure problems, the drug works on the basis of expelling certain amounts of potassium and sodium salts (which help retain water) from the body. If the patient happens to have a constitutional imbalance in their potassium/sodium metabolism in the first place, then not only will the diuretic be largely useless but, over a period of time, the patient could possibly develop some kind of nerve disorder because the nerves and nerve sheaths rely on these two mineral salts for correct nutrition. On the other hand, if we were first to consult the blueprint formula of the patient's vital essence, the relative strengths and weaknesses of potassium/sodium in their constitution would be revealed. In the case of a patient whose symptoms manifest as faulty blood pressure, the blueprint would reveal the type of materials required and the area of the individual that needs to be treated in order for a successful cure to be achieved.

One further point to consider with regard to allopathic drugs is that many of them are produced by genetic engineering. The human form is a natural organism and, as such, will not readily respond to a substance of non-organic origin. Even though inorganic material has healing properties when used in medicine, it is more beneficial when this material is obtained from a naturally occurring organism (plants, minerals, etc.) rather than from an artificially engineered source. This is because a causal element for healing needs to be present in the medicinal material in order for really efficacious healing to take place.

The crucial difference between chemical drugs and herbal medicine is that the former are largely purified and concentrated copies of naturally occurring substances, prepared or engineered in modern pharmaceutical laboratories. Herbal medicine uses the naturally occurring substances themselves.

Medical herbalists have found that the purified active principle of a substance is less effective as a medicine than its crude natural equivalent extracted from a plant. In some instances, as part of the purification process, the chemist removes certain trace elements and molecular structures from the substance because they are regarded as restricting the effect of the main active ingredient, and are therefore unimportant. These elements and molecules, however, frequently have an important balancing role to play in ensuring that the body's reaction does not go beyond the desired level at which healing takes place. Their removal during the chemical purification process also removes this natural safety device, thus clearing the way for the manifestation of so-called 'side effects'.

Many crude herbal extracts have special antibacterial properties which control rather than destroy completely the natural bacteria occurring in, for example, the intestinal tract. The presence of certain bacteria in the human body is vital in order for it to function as a healthy organism. When these bacteria are destroyed, the suppressive control they exercise is destroyed with them, and we witness the emergence on a large scale of infections such as *candida*. This is one of the drawbacks of many chemically produced drugs when compared with their natural counterparts – however well-intentioned their development and prescription may be, their use can frequently result in undesirable secondary symptoms.

At the present time, herbal medicine is experiencing something of a revival in its popularity, and many remedies with various therapeutic claims appear on the shelves of High Street health shops and chemists. Like homoeopathy, which is also becoming more widely recognized as a genuine alternative to the allopathic medical approach, the continuing efficacy of the remedies used depends upon the properly trained practitioner rather than on self-prescribing by the general public. Medicinal herbs not only function as remedies, they also affect the natural flow of energy through the body. This means that when they are taken on a daily basis as part of the body's general maintenance, rather than for any specific symptoms, the natural flow of energy can be adversely affected. (This same principle also applies to homoeopathic remedies.) A further point to bear in mind with any remedy is that, should the symptoms return once the course of treatment comes to an end, the conclusion must be drawn that the remedy has merely acted as a palliative and not acted at the level necessary for healing to take place. The root cause of the illness still remains. This particular point illustrates that the continual use of herbal remedies should be avoided. These are becoming increasingly popular, not only as alternatives to caffeine-rich tea and coffee, but also as refreshing beverages in their own right; however, their continual and uncontrolled use over a prolonged period of time may actually end up creating the very symptoms they are intended to heal.

In the practice of herbal medicine, it is rare for a herbalist to give one single remedy. Combinations of two or more herbs are the most popular form of treatment and any such combination will include herbs that are intended to act together, in unison, within the body. Their specific combination is not only based on their curative potential but also ensures that their action is gentle. For example, a demulcent (mucilaginous or oily, soothing) herb may be combined with some that are strongly aromatic. Their action also possesses the bipolar energetic qualities of *Yin* and *Yang* and they can thus be used to treat both negative and positive aspects of the body's energy system.

Herbal medicine runs parallel to nutrition, for both dietary changes and medicinal herbs can influence the biochemical balance of the physical organism. In the orthodox approach to medicine no connection is made between the two, and yet it is important, especially for those complementary practitioners who use herbal medicines, to recognize and adopt this duality of nutrition and medicine. Nutrition therapy, herbal medicine, and even prescribed drugs, in their potential to affect the body's biochemical balance, are all variations of a single therapeutic approach. Perhaps the difference lies in the fact that the complementary practitioner will always use the mildest form of medicinal remedy. Any medical practitioner must be cognizant of the body's innate ability to regain balance and health, given the correct therapeutic dosage along with any dietary change necessary to achieve the required effect. Synthetic drugs may also be used, but perhaps only in an emergency.

Nutrition itself can, of course, be a major causal factor in illness. This fact is sadly neglected by many physicians and seems to be largely absent from their medical education and training. It is therefore not surprising that many doctors are hesitant to give any nutritional advice, because it is frequently an area of which they have little knowledge, and yet the basic principles of nutritional counselling are relatively simple and should be known by the general practitioner. The same cannot be said of many of my colleagues practising in complementary medicine; irrespective of the form of therapy in which they specialize, their initial contact with a patient includes an assessment of the patient's nutrition as a normal part of the diagnosis.

It must be said, however, that things are already changing. The attitudes and views of the general public towards health and illness now frequently question the emphasis placed by conventional medicine on the use of synthetic drugs and surgery. I am sure that this too will change, perhaps to be gradually supplemented, or even replaced, by what are now regarded as the complementary therapies. Although this process may take many decades, we should not ignore what allopathic medicine has to offer through its understanding of the physical body and diagnostic processes such as scans and X-ray procedures which tell us much about the progress taking place within a patient during a course of medication.

Generally speaking, the present relationship between allopathic and complementary practitioners is less than favourable, and I look forward to the time when a complementary practitioner is able to send his or her patient along to the hospital for a scan, X-ray or other non-invasive diagnostic technique so that the efficacy of the remedies being used can be monitored. If this were possible, not only would it be easier to monitor the patient's progress but, at the same time, allopathic practitioners might become more aware of what complementary practice actually has to offer. By the same token, both allopathic and complementary practitioners might begin to put aside their differences of opinion in order to serve the individual patient more effectively according to his or her own specific needs.

Observations and Reactions

The process of monitoring the patient's progress is crucial, irrespective of whether we are administering herbal remedies or homoeopathic remedies (or even allopathic drugs). The practitioner must always have regular reports from his or her patients so that they are able to observe and evaluate what the remedy is doing. We know that when a reaction to the remedy occurs the symptoms will change, either in character or in degree. The symptoms may improve, disappear completely or, alternatively, they may even increase. Each of these changes is a manifestation of the action of the remedy upon the vital essence or vital energy of the patient.

The most common reaction after the remedy or remedies have been administered is either an aggravation or an amelioration of the patient's condition. There are two types of aggravation which may manifest within the patient. First, there is the aggravation of the actual condition of the disease to an extent that the patient feels worse. The second type of aggravation is very different, because although the symptoms become worse the patient reports that he or she is actually feeling much better within themselves. In the first instance, the aggravation of the disease combined with the worsening of the patient's own condition indicates that the disease is, in fact, growing stronger while his or her vital energy is becoming weaker. The second case, in which there is an aggravation of the symptoms whilst the patient reports feeling better, tells us that his or her vital essence is being set in order and becoming a lot stronger. Even though the individual symptoms may themselves show some aggravation, it is evident that the cause of the illness is being treated successfully and therefore we can attach less importance to the symptoms displayed by the patient.

This observation of how the aggravation or amelioration of the symptoms takes place during the healing period is important, because we are looking for a progressive healing of the patient, and an improvement in his or her quality of life. Sometimes a patient will say that he or she is getting worse and yet, on analysing the symptoms, it will be found that the reverse is in fact true. In certain instances, the story told by the symptoms has more relevance than the patient's own opinion and, if reassured about the improvement in their condition, the patient will then immediately feel better and, very often, the disappearance of the symptoms will follow shortly afterwards. In this context, the healing process is essentially one of focusing the attention of the mind, thus allowing the individual's purpose to regain control of the mind and, subsequently, the physical body.

ANTIMATTER REMEDIES: HOMOEOPATHY

Mineral Substances

In the past, homoeopathic physicians and researchers were unsure of the dynamics that mineral substances contain and how their action in their potentized form was able to effect changes in, and heal, the physical body. They considered the mineral substances to be mere fragments of those that made up the planet Earth. They also recognized that the planet was itself susceptible to activation by vital energy, to such an extent that its movements were seemingly governed by certain laws. These are the rhythmical laws within seasonal change – for example, the gravitational influence of the moon which can cause the tidal motion of the sea to rise and fall a vertical distance of more than twenty five feet around some coastlines. The same rhythmical laws apply to the birth and death of all living creatures, and to the very essence of organic and inorganic matter.

Today we are also well aware of the living and dynamic forces residing in the mass of mineral substances that make up our planet. To understand how and why a mineral substance can cause healing in the vital essence of a patient – as in the case of a colloidal mineral (celloid), for example – we need only to consider the theory of wave/particle duality and the forces that reside in matter at rest. When we fully understand in modern terms that mass (such as a mineral substance) is a form of energy – that is to say, when we no longer perceive it merely as an immutable solid – then perhaps we can also understand how the homoeopathically potentized remedy made from a natural mineral substance can affect the force fields of the patient's own mass (that is, his or her physical body). The energy within a mass can be transformed into other forms of energy. In modern physics, the accelerated collision of particles is the main tool of the high-energy physicist in studying the relationship between mass and energy. During the collision process, material particles are created and destroyed, their mass being transformed into energy.

Samuel Hahnemann, the founder of homoeopathy, used the same principle of colliding particles (albeit at a much slower speed) in the succussion techniques he developed, adding a dilution process after the collision had taken place. According to Hahnemann, the succussion–dilution process released kinetic energy (energy that depends upon movement for its effect) from the mass of the substance into the carrier vehicle – in this case, water. This kinetic energy resides in all homoeopathic medicines which, when taken orally, influence the dynamic energies of the patient. Hahnemann was a very intuitive physician, who was perhaps ahead of his time, but his theories regarding the dynamics of matter and their useful application in the medical treatment of patients can now be proven by the technology of modern physics.

Vegetable Substances

The vegetable kingdom has probably served man in his fight against disease for longer than either the mineral or animal kingdoms. In our own daily lives, we can observe and recognize the growth and movement of plants, perceiving the vital energies within them responding to the vitality of the universe with its unfolding but systematic order, and to the changing seasons and movement of the planets. In accordance with these natural laws of order, plants develop from a seed according to the physical characteristics of the parent plants and so mighty oaks (not elm or ash trees) from little acorns grow. Locked within the acorn is the genetic pattern or particle wave form of the oak – all that is needed in addition are the energies of the earth, light and ether to act as catalysts for the energy contained within the seed. The dynamic pattern of growth will unfold until, on reaching maturity, the plant produces its own seed, thus passing on the vital forces or essence of the species. This is known as the law of cycles.

My own appreciation of plant dynamics is prompted by their ability to grow against the forces of gravity – for example, the power within a tree that enables it to raise daily many gallons of water through its mass. The accomplishment of this feat gives us an indication of the unseen force contained within the vegetable kingdom, just as there are similar forces within the mineral world. These forces are now documented in the considerable amount of data recording the response of plants to stimuli such as environmental change and sound vibration; responses which range from changeable growth patterns to a plant's production of its own recordable sound vibrations. Perhaps the most obvious element in the growth pattern is the plant's response to light, a response that liberates it from the gravitational pull of the earth, so that it is able to maintain a state of equilibrium between these two forces. As we observe the vegetable kingdom, we see facts that teach us to abandon the concept of indestructible matter arising from the traditional materialistic and mechanistic views. Our study of plants reveals the fact that matter is nothing more than a fixed stage of a universal process. It is cosmic energy in a dense, arrested form.

When compared with the speed at which most human beings choose to live their lives, the rate of change and motion in the vegetable kingdom belies its continual dynamic state. Thanks to chronophotography and the time-lapse camera, we are reminded of the dynamics of a slower pace of life in which roots delve into the earth, dislodging stones and splitting rocks with considerable force, and stems swing in rhythmic circles, like ghostly arms feeling around in their surroundings for support and nutrition. Images such as these may lead us to contemplate the dynamic energy and perception residing in the world of vegetable matter, but what states of consciousness and thought processes control them? In harnessing the energy of the plant world in potentized remedies, the consciousness and thought forms of the vegetable kingdom are also harnessed, thus enabling them to act upon the consciousness and thought processes of the patient.

Animal Substances

In passing from the world of plants to that of animals, including human beings, we encounter many differences in physical form. Apart from the clearly visible external differences, the most significant distinction as far as we are concerned is the formation of internal organs in animals. The ability to develop organs places the animal species in a totally different dynamic state to those of the mineral and vegetable kingdoms, presenting us with the beginnings of duplicate energy patterns and consciousness related to organ function. This duplication gives animals an organic as well as a conscious state – an inner and outer world – an entirely new principle that represents a considerable advance on the dynamic state of the plant world.

The activity of animals is endowed with great strength and vitality. They also possess an imposing array of natural weapons and defensive secretions that can cause strong reactions in other animals as well as plants, even when prepared in minute doses. For instance, cobra venom, when diluted to one part per 1000 and injected into the vein of a fish, will stop the heart beating in twelve minutes. A dilution of one part per 100 will cause plant life to wilt and decompose. Many of these animal secretions have been found very effective in a homoeopathic potentized form for the healing of humans, and even allopathic schools of medicine recognize the efficiency of minute dosages of venom in treating several serious conditions, especially those showing disturbance of the vascular and nervous systems.

The manner in which animal, vegetable, or mineral substances act in their homoeopathic potentized form is described as follows by Herbert A. Roberts in his book *The Principles and Art of Cure by Homoeopathy*:

> When animal, vegetable or mineral substances are potentised they are rendered more potent because of the breaking up and disintegration of their atomic relationships that place them in a form where they act directly upon the dynamic force of the individual. That is, in their disintegration their energy is liberated by releasing the radioactive power. Through the radioactivity exerting itself upon the vital energy of the individual the potency is made effective.
>
> Thus we are forced to recognise different forms of energy; the discharge of different energies or rays, from what we have considered as inanimate metal and elements. We find that they respond energetically in much the same way as plants and animals; not alone in their simple state do we find this response, but again and again as they are assimilated, broken down and rebuilt in different forms of life, from the simple assimilation and complicated re-building of the plant to the profound reaction on all living substances when they are in potentised form.

The above statement, recorded nearly fifty years ago, corresponds totally with all the findings of today's physicists working in the fields of subatomic and quantum physics, just as the descriptions of the vital essence from bygone days still stand firm when compared with today's understanding.

Remedies and the Vital Essence

When we describe the vital essence as a trinity, or tri-unity, of three distinctive aspects – *purpose, mind, body* – and acknowledge the interdependent nature of their being, we must not lose sight of their unity right from the moment of conception when the coming together of two parent cells, themselves each containing a vital essence, gives individuality of essence to the foetus. The act of conception provides the vehicle in which the vital essence will dwell, for the essence exists before the parent cells conjoin, having chosen the parents because of its need for a particular environment (including race and country) and a particular point in time for the physical manifestation.

Minerals, plants and animals each have their own dynamic states; so, too, do human beings. In previous chapters we have examined something of the dynamic relationship existing between the three dimensions – purpose, mind and body – of the individual, as well as the thought forms and conscious attitudes related to his or her vital essence. The dynamics of this relationship will obviously play an important role in our treatment of the patient by energetic remedies.

We have already proposed that both the purpose and mind of the individual exist at the level of the wave form. The mind, including its thought processes and attitudes, can be influenced by mental and emotional activity as well as the wave forms emanating from the purpose. The purpose is the innermost part of the being and that part which, so to speak, chooses to manifest as physical form at a particular time in the earth's unfolding evolutionary process and within that of the universe as a whole. For practitioners working within this vast process, it is important to consider the vital essence of the patient as well as the picture presented by his or her personality. The latter rarely corresponds to the inner being or purpose, and often they occur as two distinctive or separate vibrational aspects. The prescription of remedies or other treatment should be matched to the whole individual – to the purpose as well as the personality – for perhaps many of the failures experienced by practitioners are due to treating the personality on its own. Disease arises from disharmony between the vital essence and the physical personality. In helping the patient to regain optimum health, the remedy should allow the total expression of the vital essence through a balanced personality; the vibration of the remedy should therefore be one of self-expression as well as healing.

It is now being realized that the vital essence of the individual manifests its deepest levels in a symbolic manner, giving us recognizable clues to its deeper attitudes and consciousness. This symbolic manifestation consists of the mind, with its mental activity in the form of logic and discriminative thinking; the emotional aspect, with its desires and ambitions; and the mass of the physical body which is the arrested dynamic state of these various energies. These three aspects remind us of the Ayurvedic *tridoshas* (or trinities) in that they will react to, and benefit from, selected vibrations of flower, herbal or homoeopathic remedies derived from the mineral, vegetable and animal kingdoms (see p. 67).

Every individual is a unique integration of *essence* and *substance*, or non-material and material elements, the energizing of which is governed by universal laws that can compensate for continued environmental changes. This uniqueness of the individual led Dr Hahnemann to suggest remedies to match the individuality of his patients and the variation in potency of homoeopathic remedies takes into account the different vibrational levels of the individual. The higher potencies act in the higher energy fields of the patient and are more suitable for chronic and constitutional conditions, while the lower potencies act in areas of greater density and are better suited to the more material and acute conditions that occur at a physical or biological level. Hahnemann also based his remedies on the law of similars, following the principle of the minimum dose. The law of similars, or 'like cures like', acknowledges that the symptoms produced in a healthy person as a reaction to a mineral, vegetable or animal substance will, if displayed by a sick person, disappear when the same substance is administered to them.

The method for producing the medicinal substance in homoeopathic form is briefly as follows. The substance is measured and one part is diluted with either nine or ninety nine parts of the diluting vehicle, depending on whether the decimal (10) or centesimal (100) scale is being used. The vehicle is a non-medicinal or inert substance such as sac lac (sugar of milk) or rectified spirit. This is followed by a process of trituration (pulverization) in the case of sac lac or succussion (shaking) for liquids (processes now done by machine but done by hand in Hahnemann's day) and the resulting material or liquid form of the remedy is then scaled as either 1x (decimal) or 1c (centesimal). The process is then repeated, each time raising the potency – 2c, 3c, 4c and so on. By the time a potency of around 12c is reached, there is no molecular presence of the original substance remaining and yet many remedies are used at potencies of 30c, 100c or even higher, with great efficacy.

The principle of 'like cures like' can be illustrated with the bee sting. Perhaps readers have experienced the symptoms it produces – burning, stinging and excessive swelling which are followed by stiffness, constriction, difficulty in breathing and general oedema. When the homoeopathically prepared Apis or bee venom is administered to a patient suffering from rheumatism, kidney disease or peritonitis, a cure is rapidly effected.

The above concepts are solid foundations on which to base an understanding of prescribing remedies to match the patient's symptoms, but I wonder how Hahnemann would have dealt with the additional symptoms and conditions that face us today? We only have to look around us to see patients suffering from the effects of the same allopathic drugs that were intended to control their original symptoms; symptoms that are nothing other than indicators or warnings of underlying causes and problems which end up being driven deeper into the vital essence, thus causing yet further symptoms and aggravations. I wonder, too, what Hahnemann would have made of modern environmental stress, allergies, food additives, toxins used in agriculture, artificial colourings that cause hyperactivity in children, and so on? The list could go on and on!

One further point regarding homoeopathic remedies; as the potency of the remedy increases through successive repetitions of the succussion–dilution process, so its field of action is changed as well. The higher the potency, the closer the remedy is to the realm in which wave forms affect particles – the realm of quantum electrodynamics.

THE NEW ENERGETIC MEDICINE

The future for energetic medicine lies in the area where the subtle formative forces of nature are at work on an unseen level. We have mentioned that, above a certain potency, the homoeopathic remedies produced by the succussion–dilution process contain no molecular structure of the original matter, and yet they can and do heal the physical body. Their efficacy must lie in their ability to promote change in the wave form vibrations that control matter – the realm of spinning electrons and the photon 'messenger'. I have always considered homoeopathic medicine to be coded instructions contained in a carrier vehicle which are utilized within the physical body of the patient at the deepest level of formative energy. But if homoeopathic medicine contains pure wave form, would it not be possible to simulate the effect by using an instrument that corresponds to the same principles as the unseen worlds of quantum electrodynamics? By addressing these concepts, I was able to develop the Base 64 light-activated simulator.

In an earlier chapter it was explained that the blueprint or vital essence provides the pattern of causation for the individual patient at a formative level. The ideal, therefore, was to use the blueprint symbolically in an instrument whose principles are influenced by those of quantum physics to restore the patient's energetic pattern by a simulation technique. If we regard thought as a dimension of activity not governed by the laws of space-time (relativity) but capable of manifesting according to the principles of wave/particle duality, then perhaps a thought could be represented at a symbolic level by a recognizable symbol that is, in turn, capable of triggering the very thought it symbolized. With this in mind, an experiment was conducted to establish whether a numerical symbol, for example, activated by a light source (photon) would produce the desired effect in a medium or vehicle such as sac lac and then, having done that, to see if it acted like a conventional homoeopathic remedy when administered to a patient. The experiment proved successful.

The symbol used in the experiment utilized the principle of wave/particle duality in the context (outlined on page 41) of sound being a measurable wave form that can manifest as wave (sound vibration) or particle (named object or person). Homoeopathic practitioners would know the efficacy of a

remedy such as Aconitum napellus when produced by the succussion–dilution process from the original substance (monks-
hood), but how can this be effectively conveyed by the use of
a symbol? The production of the symbol is quite straightforward
and uses the letter/number values shown in Chart 2 (p. 41) as
follows. Note that 'C' has a numerical value of 11 which
becomes 2 (1+1). Other two-digit numerical values are added
to produce a single digit.

$$\text{ACONITUM NAPELLUS} = \frac{A \quad O \quad I \quad U}{C \quad N \quad T \quad M} \quad \frac{A \quad E \quad \quad U}{N \quad P \quad LL \quad S} =$$

$$= \frac{1 \quad 7 \quad 1 \quad 6}{2 \quad 5 \quad 4 \quad 4} \quad \frac{1 \quad 5 \quad \quad 6}{5 \quad 8 \quad 33 \quad 3} =$$

$$\frac{15}{15} \qquad \frac{12}{22} =$$

$$\frac{6}{6} \qquad \frac{3}{4} =$$

$$\frac{9}{1}$$

The symbolic numbers are then written in washable ink on a
special laminated card as shown in Figure 11(a). The name of
the simulated remedy is also written on the top of the card.
Another card is prepared as in Figure 11(b) to give the potency
or strength for the simulated remedy decided upon by the practitioner. The hole at the centre of the card is to allow a beam
of light to pass through.

One additional advantage of this method of simulation when
used in normal practice is that the practitioner preparing the
remedy will usually know the patient and, in some cases, the
blueprint of his or her vital essence. If the practitioner has one
or the other in his or her mind (consciously or unconsciously)
while preparing the symbol, the card will additionally be tuned
to the vibrational wave length of the patient or of his or her
blueprint.

The Base 64 simulator uses the principle of Young's *Interference Experiment* (otherwise known as the *two slit* experiment)
first conducted way back towards the beginning of the nineteenth century. In Young's experiment, a small source of light
projects a ray of light waves through two narrow parallel slits
in an opaque screen towards a second screen. Instead of an

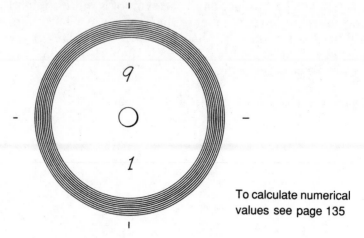

Figure 11a   Base 64 card for *Aconitum napellus*

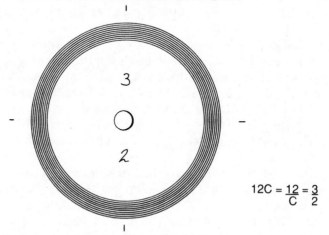

Figure 11b   Base 64 card for potency 12c

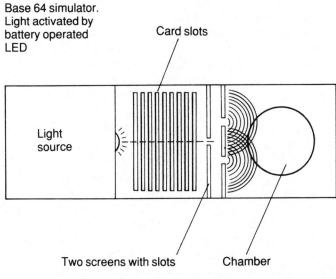

Figure 12 The base 64 simulator

even distribution of light being produced on the second screen, we end up with a series of alternating light and dark stripes due to the light waves interfering with each other. Where they arrive in step, they reinforce each other; where they arrive out of step, they cancel each other out. The interference pattern of the waves is clearly dependent on there being two slits in the screen for if one or the other is blocked off, the interference pattern disappears.

When a source is used to project particles (for example electrons), the same pattern of interference is produced, even when they are projected singly, one at a time. (In the case of particles, the regulated speed at which they are projected – in other words, the time lapse between the projection of each particle – corresponds to a measurable wavelength.) The curious thing here is that when they are sent through the slits one at a time we would naturally expect them to pass through one slit or the other and yet, in fact, it appears that the particle passes through *both* slits at the same time for the interference pattern is produced equally by a large number of particles and by the impact of a single particle. In other words, the single particle must carry with it an image of both slits in the form of a wave, which it brings into existence by imprinting it in the form of a pattern on the second screen. Of course, in quantum physics there is always the uncertainty principle to contend with but, in the circumstances, the only conclusion we can draw from the experiment is that we are in effect witnessing the simultaneous co-existence of both wave and particle aspects of light . . . and of matter and antimatter.

To translate this effect into the context of remedy simulation, we need to recall that thought is also a wave form susceptible to the phenomenon of wave/particle duality. If we therefore transmit a wave form imprinted with a thought or symbol, as in our experimental instrument, then the wave form will carry with it the particle aspect related to that same thought or symbol. In the experiment, the symbolic thought of Aconitum napellus was imprinted on the wave form so that when the particles came into contact with the sac lac in the chamber they imprinted the particle aspect of Aconitum napellus on the carrier vehicle for the remedy. How does this happen?

We can illustrate the process using the analogy of a game of tennis and, at the same time, recalling the phenomenon of 'action at a distance' (see p. 73). In tennis, the action of the players is dictated by the ball as it passes from one player to the other. Similarly, electrons are affected by the 'ball' (in this case, the photon) that is exchanged between them. In the remedy simulation experiment, the electrons spinning around the nuclei of the sac lac in the chamber were affected by the 'messenger' photons emitted from the incoming particles and thus received the imprint of the image or thought the latter were carrying with them. In this way, the sac lac itself now carried the wave/particle thought of Aconitum napellus.

The remedy simulation experiment may appear to have more to do with the realms of science fiction than the world of medical science but, nevertheless, it worked. The process used to produce simulated remedies for patients corresponds exactly to sophisticated field theories and the wave/particle duality of quantum electrodynamics, a subject which the interested reader will find expressed more fully in the books included in the suggestions for further reading. One important factor we need to mention again here, and which was mentioned earlier in connection with the EPR experiment (see p. 73), is that in quantum physics the observer is an integral part of the experiment and the effect that he or she chooses to look for plays a crucial role in deciding the experiment's outcome. This phenomenon also occurs in the remedy simulation process because the practitioner, in the course of operating the instrument and preparing the remedy, is very much an integral part of the process. In other words, he or she chooses what happens by imprinting their own thought forms and choice upon the procedure.

Over the last four years the Base 64 system has evolved from its earlier experimentation with simulating remedies to a stage where it now produces remedies containing imprints of the patient's complete blueprint in order to activate their own vital essence according to its original purpose. The system can also treat specific areas at the mental, emotional or physical levels which have been pinpointed by orthodox or complementary diagnostic procedures.

To sum up the Base 64 system in a few words: it uses metaphysical science and knowledge to analyse the causal factor in the patient's ill health, and modern physics and science to produce the wave/particle remedies it employs as part of the healing process.

CHAPTER 6

Subtle Meridians or Thought Strings

From the perspective of the modern twentieth-century Western world, it would seem that science and technology have provided us with answers to most of the questions confronting mankind. As the physical world has yielded up its secrets, so we have devised increasingly refined aids to help us probe further into realms previously inaccessible to the human eye, whether in the domain of subatomic particles or the farthest reaches of the universe. It now seems only a matter of time before further refined technological advances will provide us with answers to the remaining questions, maybe even with the 'ultimate theory' giving us the definitive explanation for the origin of the universe and everything in it.

There is a difference, however, between the factual knowledge accessible to all and the knowledge gained by the individual through his or her own personal experience – for even though, at times, we may appear to share identical experiences or witness the same events, the more subtle levels and effects of these phenomena are unique for each and every one of us. As a result of this I believe that in whatever direction future scientific theory or research may lead us, it is essential for it to take into account the individual as well as the universal.

For thousands of years, the principal concerns of metaphysical theory have found their expression in the idea of microcosm–macrocosm and the instructive phrase '*Know thyself*'. The underlying concept contained in these two aspects of metaphysics is the notion that knowledge of ourselves is simultaneously knowledge of the universe, and knowledge of the universe is simultaneously knowledge of ourselves. This parallel between individual and universal knowledge does not, however, refer simply to the external appearances of the physical world, but to its more subtle dimensions as well; that is, to what is called the *inner* as opposed to the *outer* world. As human beings, our knowledge and experience of the relationship between these two worlds can provide us with an understanding of our own individual purpose in life as well as our true function in the universal order of things.

These two apparently distinctive worlds meet in the manifestation of physical form and it is in this area that we encounter one of the greatest remaining mysteries – the origin of form itself. In previous chapters we have examined various aspects of this mystery in the light of certain scientific and metaphysical theories which have respectively provided explanations concerning the physical and pre-physical dimensions of existence. In simple scientific terms, the question of the origin of form can be expressed by asking what additional factor is it that enables a collection of molecules to assemble themselves into the human form, with all the right parts in the right places? Does this same factor enable cells to 'know' they have to become blood cells, as opposed to cells in the liver, bones or nervous system? Our knowledge of DNA implies that the plan for the human form is molecular in nature and lies within the genetic code; and yet, even though different parts of the body develop differently from each other, the DNA is the same throughout the entire individual human organism.

Science may have succeeded in providing us with a biological map of both the genetic code and the central nervous system of the human body, but one factor that has so far eluded the scientific approach is a successful explanation for the behavioural pattern of the organism. For example, if the matter (material aspect) of the central nervous system can act upon the mind (that is, in producing sensation), can mind also act upon matter? If this is the case, then it follows that the transmission of correct or incorrect thought impulses could similarly affect the molecular structure of the genetic code.

This is where I feel the Base 64 system and its blueprint formula contribute towards solving some existing problems because, in providing a new model to analyse the cause of human illness and disease, of necessity it presents a possible explanation for the behaviour and underlying cause of the human form. Although there is nothing particularly new in the central proposition that cause equals effect, perhaps there is in the method in which the equation is used in the search to understand more about the cause of human illness. In other words, through understanding the causation of an individual's behaviour or aspirations in the form of an immutable blueprint and comparing this with the variations revealed in their current situations, we are able to construct the equation of cause equals effect, thus arriving at the true cause of the physical symptoms.

THE MERIDIANS OR THOUGHT STRINGS

The proposed biomedical model examined in these chapters has its basis in scientific and metaphysical theories and also accords with the philosophies of both Eastern and Western traditions. The most significant element in its development is the incorporation of the subtle meridians appearing as pathways of active thought between the energy centres that control the gland and organ systems. Twenty of the twenty-two meridians act as pathways between the energy centres, while the other two provide the input and output for the model. These last two are only used at the formation and dissolution of the total energy system. At one level this dissolution occurs as the endergonic transference of the energetic system to the formation of the next cell within the physical form; that is, as normal cell metabolism. At another level it takes place when the earthly life of the physical form comes to an end and the energetic system moves on to *Daath* (0-zero).

At present, research is being carried out into the relationship between the twenty principal meridians or thought strings and the twenty amino acids in DNA. The latter, in forming proteins, provide us with the building blocks of life and it has been suggested that their activity may be adversely affected by the events, thoughts and traumas of our everyday lives. Conversely, their activity may be corrected by positive thinking or certain 'seed thoughts'. It was mentioned earlier that the thought of fear will produce the hormone epinephrine and, in a similar way, the thought of hesitation or the inability to face the reality of a given situation will impair the formation of the amino acid

L-Histidine. At a physical level this will affect the production of proteins in the body but, at a subtle level, it will also affect Meridian 1, thus inhibiting the biochemistry and consciousness in the areas governed by the Centres or Categories 1 and 9. These conscious attitudes, along with those related to the other Centres, and their aspirational aspects are described in Chapter 2 under the Categories 1 to 9 (see pp. 46–58). The principal thoughts associated with the twenty-two meridians are outlined in Chapter 3 (pp. 75–88).

In exploring the relationship between the meridians, thoughts, conscious attitudes and biochemistry, the following reference table provides at a glance the biochemic/mineral elements associated with the meridians and energy centres. These elements can be used singly or as compounds in the form of mineral celloids, biochemic tissue salts or homoeopathic potencies to activate the relevant meridian.

Meridian or Thought String No.	Categories or Centres	Biochemic Minerals (see below)	Suggested Potencies
1	9 to 1	CP, MP	30c
2	9 to 8	CP, IP	30c
3	1 to 8	MP, IP	30c
4	1 to 4	MP, CF	6c
5	1 to 3	MP, PP, CS	6c
6	1 to 2	MP, IP, SIL	6c
7	1 to 6	MP, CP, SC	6c
8	1 to 5	MP, PS, PC	6c
9	1 to 7	MP, SS, SP	6c
10	8 to 7	IP, SS, SP	6c
11	8 to 5	IP, PS, PC	6c
12	8 to 6	IP, CP, SC	6c
13	8 to 2	IP, SIL	6c
14	8 to 3	IP, PP, CS	6c
15	8 to 4	IP, CF	6c
16	4 to 7	CF, SS, SP	6c
17	7 to 3	SS, SP, PP, CS	6c
18	3 to 5	PP, CS, PC, PS	6c
19	5 to 2	PS, PC, IP, SIL	6c
20	2 to 6	IP, CP, SC, SIL	6c
21	6 to 0	CP, SC	100c
22	0 to 9	CP (females – PC)	100c

Abbreviations of biochemic minerals with tissue salts in brackets (The tissue salts are normally a 6x potency of the mineral.)

CP	Calcium Phosphate	(Calc. Phos.)
MP	Magnesium Phosphate	(Mag. Phos.)
SP	Sodium Phosphate	(Nat. Phos.)
PP	Potassium Phosphate	(Kali. Phos.)
IP	Iron Phosphate	(Ferr. Phos.)
SC	Sodium Chloride	(Nat. Mur.)
CF	Calcium Fluoride	(Calc. Fluor.)
CS	Calcium Sulphate	(Calc. Sulph.)
PS	Potassium Sulphate	(Kali. Sulph.)
SS	Sodium Sulphate	(Nat. Sulph.)
PC	Potassium Chloride	(Kali. Mur.)
SIL	Silica Dioxide	(Silica)

The various components in the reference table are used in the following manner. For example, the energetic flow of Meridian 16 which links Centres 4 and 7 is affected by thoughts arising from the difficulties experienced within our own destiny, or from our inability to face the reality of events that seem to be beyond our control. When these thoughts are aroused by the situation in which we find ourselves, they will impair the correct cell metabolism in the areas governed by Centre/Category 4 (left side of head, central nervous system, ears and nose) and Centre/Category 7 (kidneys, adrenal glands and spinal column). As will be noted from the above table, the biochemic minerals utilized in the metabolic activity of these cells are Calcium Fluoride, Sodium Sulphate and Sodium Phosphate.

The process will work in reverse when the cell metabolism is affected by, for example, some environmental activity or drug intervention that prevents normal cell nutrition. This will then cause the same thoughts to come to mind (difficulties within our own destiny, an inability to face the reality of everyday events, etc.). In both these examples we find our equation of cause equals effect: in the first instance, mind affects the behaviour of matter whereas, in the second, matter affects the behaviour of the mind.

CASE HISTORIES

The following case histories illustrate the way in which the various elements we have been examining are brought together and put to work in the healing of patients. Each case was assessed by the Base 64 system and treated by the blueprint approach, using either mineral therapy or the Base 64 energetic system of medicine. For the sake of anonymity, patients' names have been changed.

Rose

Present age 70
Age at first consultation 67
Medical history Manic depression and exhaustion for thirty years; numbness in limbs; headaches, tinnitis.
Orthodox medical opinion Manic depressive.
Orthodox medical treatment Hospitalization on many occasions. Predominantly drug therapy – lithium 800 milligrams per day and thyroxine 75 micrograms per day, both continuously over the last fourteen years.

To restore the patient's blueprint by overcoming the influence of the present environment on both the cellular and mind aspects, a pattern of treatment was used which included the aspirations and seed thoughts from the relevant categories and meridians. The actual pattern was provided by a sequence of symbolic cards set up in the Base 64 instrument (for explanation, see p. 138). The card placed in the last slot was marked 'Vital Essence' and the related numerical values were written in the blank circles in an anticlockwise direction, as illustrated in Figure 13.

The following additional Base 64 cards were also placed in the instrument:

Crown	1	Meridian	2
Meridian	7	Alta major	9
Solar plexus	6	Meridian	1
Meridian	12	Crown	1
Spleen	8		

(Note: A list of cards is available upon request, see Useful Addresses).

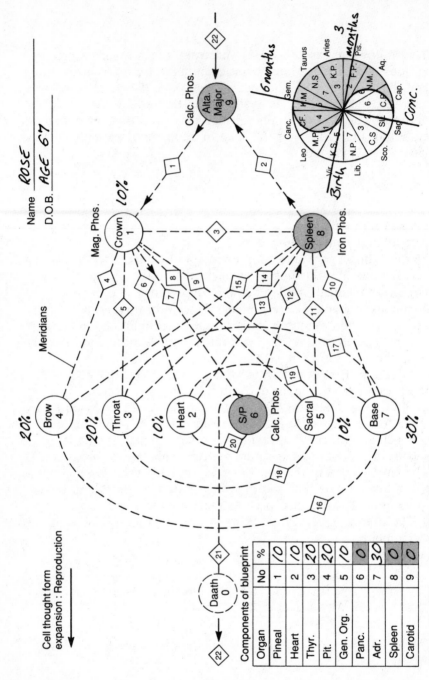

Figure 13 The patient's blueprint: 'Rose'

Vital essence components for Rose

VITAL ESSENCE *Rose*

BASE 64 BASE 64 BASE 64 BASE 64 BASE 64

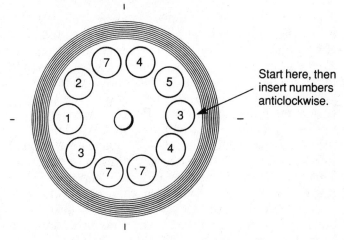

Start here, then insert numbers anticlockwise.

Figure 14 The vital essence: Base 64 card for 'Rose'

The above sequence would provide the following subtle instruction when activated into the sac lac tablets and taken orally:

Crown	1	The willpower to overcome the present situation.
Meridian	7	Creation of more self-esteem and the will to succeed via the personality.
Solar plexus	6	More devotion to family members and overcoming of selfishness and jealousy arising from all that has happened in the past; the ability to cope when things go wrong.
Meridian	12	Inner contentment; flexibility because of the changes in life.
Spleen	8	Restoration of mental and emotional balance and stability.
Meridian	2	Passiveness and new creativity; the taking up of an art or craft.
Alta major	9	Appreciation of attained life; review the world of nature and the role of humanity within the universe.
Meridian	1	Continue to strive for inner willpower; self-control for new development of health and

		strength; communication with male side (communicate more with husband).
Crown	1	Return to willpower and the strength to overcome.

The remedy thus prepared was taken orally (two pills per day in the morning) and the above pattern was also used during my consultation with Rose as I led her to understand her true self. To help her further in this undertaking, I used the relevant mineral compounds – in particular for Category 3 as the drug lithium affects the thyroid metabolism. The Category 3 remedy that seemed appropriate was Potassium Phosphate. The following mineral/biochemic supplement was administered orally in the form of celloid minerals – Magnesium Phosphate, Calcium Phosphate, Iron Phosphate, as well as the Potassium Phosphate. This was also used as a biochemic compound in the 6x and 6c ranges. The lithium and thyroxine were very slowly reduced over a period of six to seven months whilst the mineral and biochemic compounds were adjusted in quantity and strength over the same period, according to her rate of progress.

Rose's response to the treatment was excellent and she now enjoys the complete health and vitality appropriate to someone of her age. Her will to live and to love and enjoy her family and husband has also returned and she no longer takes the lithium or thyroxine, the side effects of which have gone too. The time required for the transition was approximately twelve months.

Sometimes the process can be very much faster, as was the case in our second example. Madeleine was suffering from severe headaches that were connected with menopausal problems.

Madeleine

Present age 41
Age at first consultation 40
Medical history Fibroids (not chronic); flooding during menstruation and spotting between periods.
Orthodox medical opinion Menopause.
Orthodox medical treatment Hormone replacement therapy

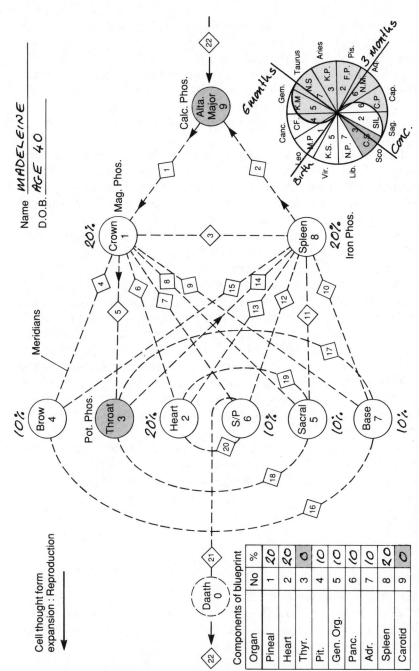

Figure 15 The patient's blueprint: 'Madeleine'

(HRT) resulting in severe migraines. HRT was discontinued in the April and Madeleine consulted me in the July, as orthodox medicine had no further suggestions for her.

In Madeleine's case, treatment used was oral mineral therapy to activate the consciousness of the energy centres and the minerals within her own physical body. The chart can also be constructed by placing the minerals next to the respective energy centres.

The treatment took the form of a biochemic tissue salt compound of the phosphates at 6x potency (Magnesium Phosphate, Potassium Phosphate, Iron Phosphate and Calcium Phosphate) with a celloid mineral compound of Potassium Phosphate and Iron Phosphate to activate Meridian 14, as it was important to bring partnerships into harmony because of the aggressive attitude towards her husband which needed controlling.

After one month Madeleine reported no further headaches, no hot flushes, and no agoraphobia or emotional disturbance. A year further on and the status of her health has been maintained without any further treatment. For me, this is a good illustration of the fact that once the cells have been rebalanced with the desired aspirations of the blueprint, the endergonic process continues in a flawless manner with the various dimensions of the individual interacting harmoniously. Even when perfect health has been regained, it is still possible for a reversal to occur if further stress or environmental changes exist for any persistent period of time.

Another patient who is experiencing considerable relief after treatment is Ann, a young woman from a perhaps overcaring family, and a wealthy background. Ann was single and had been suffering from long-term stomach disorders.

Ann

Present age 24
Age at first consultation 23
Medical history Variable bowel movements; poor skin condition; nausea; flatulence. She had been showing these symptoms for the previous two years.
Orthodox medical opinion Allergies.

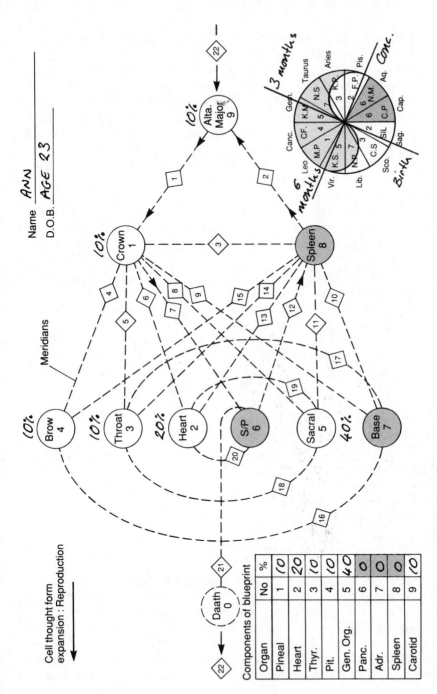

Figure 16 The patient's blueprint: 'Ann'

Orthodox medical treatment   Antibiotics and indigestion pills, neither of which had had any effect.

This case indicated a Category 6 causation, for 6 occurred as an aspiration in Ann's Category Chart as well as in her Biochemic Quadrant Chart. A further interesting factor was presented by the stomach symptoms and related skin condition which led me to take into consideration Meridian 12, linking Centres 6 and 8. Ann was given remedies of Calcium Phosphate and Iron Phosphate, along with a specially prepared remedy to include Meridian 12. This was in order to provide an element of adaptability because Ann was now alone in a big city, away from the caring parents and considerable material comforts that were part of her family background. It would also bring contentment in viewing life from a perspective other than one centred on wealth.

The changes were slow but, with the aid of a herbal stomach mixture and perseverance with the mineral remedies, a breakthrough was obtained and the symptoms disappeared.

When illness or disease do occur, they are often the doorway to the patient's own true reality and to the realization of their goals and aspirations – something that has been experienced by those patients who have faced the reality of their illness. One such patient was Pattie who first consulted me in 1987.

Pattie

Present age   43
Age at first consultation   38
Medical history   Breast cancer, origin unknown.
Orthodox medical opinion   Unfavourable. The cancer was appearing to spread.
Orthodox medical treatment   Mastectomy; radiation therapy.

When Pattie first came to see me she had recently had a mastectomy and was currently undergoing radiation therapy. She was receiving the best of private medical care but the prognosis was not good and I was consulted for an opinion. My initial finding on interpreting Pattie's chart was that with a cancer occurring where it had, and with her particular desired aspirations (Categories 6, 8 and 3), the cause of the disease appeared to lie in the attitudes she displayed at that time. These

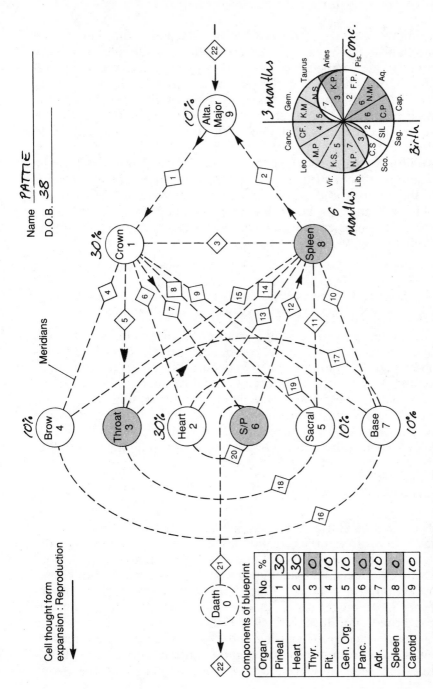

Figure 17 The patient's blueprint: 'Pattie'

attitudes were characterized by an extremely materialistic and mechanistic approach to life which, considering her very comfortable financial background, was a perfectly understandable approach. In fact, Pattie was not the first patient I had met with this approach and this type of illness. The disease itself had been a great shock to her whole system; the kind of shock that makes us call out, 'Why me? What have I done to deserve this?'.

Pattie's case struck me as an ideal opportunity to use the blueprint theory of healing the individual by effecting a change of incorrect attitudes and thoughts. Her illness was such that a radical change in her thinking was called for and therefore counselling was employed using the elements of correct thinking from the following categories:

Category 3   To concentrate on the more abstract and philosophical aspects of life.
Category 6   A major event causing a total shift in career or hobbies.
Category 8   Relaxing the rigid boundaries of her thinking.

Oral remedies of Potassium Chloride, Calcium Phosphate, and Iron Phosphate were used, as well as Vitamin C in high doses and pancreatic enzymes (see Appendix 2 and Further Reading). Within a few months, dramatic changes had occurred. Four years later, the patient is a leader in promoting lectures on Eastern teachings from overseas. She takes an interest in the healing arts and is caring for her fellow human beings but, most of all, she is healthy and leading a happy and fulfilling family life.

NON-LOCALIZED EFFECTS

These case histories illustrate something which is all too rarely taken into account when patients are treated according to the orthodox biomedical model and this is the phenomenon of non-localized effects, an example of what we have referred to earlier as 'action at a distance'. One thing that current ecological concerns have taught us is that, even where our own planet is concerned, non-localized effects are a reality that cannot be ignored – acid rain causing the death of forests hundreds of miles away from the source of the pollution; agricultural chemicals that seep into ground-water; the depletion of the ozone

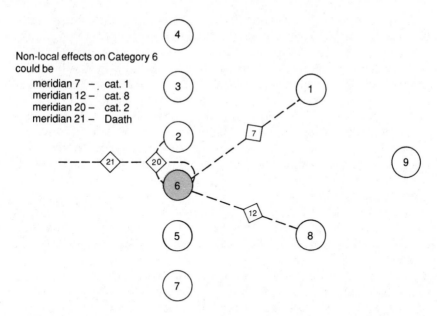

Figure 18 Non-local effects of Category/Centre 6

layer some twelve miles above the earth, and so on. Of course, it is easy enough to suggest that the cause of these ecological symptoms lies in industrial pollutants of one kind or another, when perhaps the real cause is simply human ignorance or short-sightedness on a grand scale. It is certainly one way of learning that the effects of our actions are not restricted to the immediate arena of the original action and, following on from this, it may lead to a wider acceptance of the idea that the physical symptoms of disease do not necessarily manifest at the site of their cause.

When a patient with gall bladder symptoms or ileo-caecal valve (ICV) syndrome consults an orthodox medical prac-titioner, they will probably be told, without hesitation, that the problem is localized in the gall bladder and little or no consider-ation will be given to any other area of the body. However, the subtle system of energetic meridians and centres of activity does provide us with instant access to non-localized effects. For example, gall bladder or ICV symptoms which come under Category 6, the solar plexus, are linked to other areas and categories by the meridians and certain thoughts.

Figure 18 shows some of the areas connected to the solar

plexus (6). The patient may be experiencing congested emotions, or disharmony in the mental/emotional states at 8, which corresponds to their inflexibility at a time when change is occurring in their lives. Both these factors will inhibit the flow of life's natural energy along Meridian 12, thus restricting the two-way energetic link between Centres 6 and 8. Our life energy flows constantly through the layers of our subtle body in a way that is identical to the circulation of our life-giving blood through the veins and arteries of our physical body. As we know, at a physical level, when the flow of blood in our body becomes congested or blocked, the repercussions can be very serious. The same applies to the flow of life's energy through the meridians or arteries of our subtle body. Therefore, in our example of the gall bladder, one can never say that the cause of the symptoms lies solely within that specific organ system.

The same applies to what many physicians regard as the major causes of death in our society today – heart disease, cancer, high blood pressure, and so on. All of these are symptoms of a deeper cause, namely our general life style with its emphasis on over-indulgence, self-interested goals, and the continual clamour of the ego for materialistic fulfilment of one kind or another – a life style which, by its very nature, chooses to ignore the reality of a deeper purpose to life, whether this is seen to be the life of the individual human being or the continuing evolutionary life of the human race.

It must be said, however, that physicians are not the only ones who cling to the conventional concept of medicine. A large proportion of the general public does so as well, which means, at least for the time being, that medical research can continue largely in its present form because that is what its adherents demand. The much-needed breakthrough in medicine will only come about when medical researchers regain their spirit of adventure and discovery, going beyond the drug-oriented research stipulated by the multinational drug houses.

THE FLOW OF LIFE

There is one significant element that would appear to separate the dominant train of thought in the complementary approach to medicine from that of its orthodox counterpart: a sense of continuing purpose to life. In previous chapters we have considered various aspects of the element of purpose with regard to healing the individual patient but, hopefully without becoming embroiled in too many philosophical issues, we can go on to say that the purpose of the individual cannot be detached from the evolutionary purpose of humanity as a whole, nor from the evolution of the natural world. One useful barometer for measuring the divergent opinions and attitudes that questions such as this arouse is the role given to consciousness and the mind within the flow of life.

Current areas of debate include controversy over such matters as the point at which life really begins and ends; whether animals experience any form of consciousness; and the degree to which the process of natural selection is, or is not, the explanation for the emergence of new species. But where once other sciences would have allowed themselves to be guided by the work of physicists, now that quantum physics gives the mind (individual and universal) a prominent role in the flow of life many aspects of modern science, including chemistry and biology, seem determined to abolish the influence of the mind altogether. Modern physicists, experiencing the compelling evidence of mind and thought influence at a quantum level, are moving away from the rigid order of the mechanistic model of humanity whereas biologists, who once suggested a position for the human mind in nature's hierarchy, are heading towards a reductionist and material model, based largely on the physics of the nineteenth century. At the present time it appears as though biologists and physicists are heading in two different directions in their view of humanity.

As we mentioned earlier with regard to light and the phenomenon of wave/particle duality, light can either be measured as a wave or as a particle but not as both at the same time (see p. 71). The source of light (the light bulb) does not exist in one reality to emit one, and in another reality to emit the other: it remains constant. So it is with humanity. Whether we choose to agree with the biologists or the physicists, the reality of humanity does not change. It is the perception and understanding of it that changes from the viewpoint of one observer to the next and, as each of us has our own perception and understanding of reality (whether human or otherwise) arising from our individual experience of it, it is not surprising that disagreements abound.

From my own personal viewpoint, the future of medicine lies in the various interested parties – orthodox and complementary practitioners, biologists, chemists, physicists, and others – agreeing to agree on the common ground they share in their mutual concern for the future of medicine, rather than simultaneously pulling it this way and that, like children tugging for possession of a rag doll. A key factor in this, as in the narrower context of the continuing health of the individual patient, is the recognition of *purpose*, for without this all-important element there is no ongoing dimension or dynamic. On this point both science and religion agree: we are here for a purpose. As for the ongoing dynamic – in other words, the continuing flow of life – the one expresses it in evolutionary terms, the other as eternity or life after and beyond death. Here science and religion may choose to differ regarding their perception and understanding of these phenomena, and in the language in which they express them, but the reality of life's purpose and flow remains constant. In spite of these views expressed by Western scientific and religious thought, Western civilization seemingly contradicts itself through its preoccupation with the apparent finality of death; the contradiction being that to view death as the end of it all is to deny life's purpose and flow.

In the blueprint formula the dimension of purpose and its ongoing dynamic, the continuing flow of life, is represented by the symbol '0' which is referred to as *Daath*, a Qabalistic word signifying a dimension of accumulated experiences. As explained in Chapter 3 in connection with Meridians 21 and 22, this dimension of accumulated experiences refers simultaneously to the 'memory bank' of information transmitted from one cell to the next in cellular reproduction and, at the level of the individual human being, to the next dimension of life. We can express this another way by saying that in Meridian 21, *Daath* signifies the point of 'output' of free energy from one cell to the next (or one dimension of existence to the next) at the end of a cycle, and in Meridian 22 it denotes the point of 'input' of free energy at the beginning of a new cycle. In this sense, the blueprint formula includes an element which transcends the finality of death.

Whether we choose to understand this last point from the

scientific viewpoint as being part of the evolutionary process, or from the religious perspective as spiritual renewal, will depend largely on our own individual perception and understanding of these things. Perhaps there is a common ground where it is possible for these two views to reach some degree of agreement whilst retaining the integrity of their own distinctive identity and perspective? In other words, instead of perpetuating unnecessarily the apparent conflict between science and religion, can their joint knowledge and wisdom serve to broaden and enrich our understanding of humanity and its purpose here on earth? Here we can return to the 'barometer' we mentioned earlier in this chapter: the role given to consciousness and the mind within the flow of life, adding to this the role envisaged for the element of 'purpose' or 'spirit'.

Since Charles Darwin presented an overwhelming mass of evidence in favour of biological evolution, a succession of scientists have theorized that all life, including humanity, is the result of chance variation. This takes the form of random mutation and natural selection: a view which is, of course, the cornerstone of modern evolutionary thought. According to this theory, the human ability to think and reason is no more than the peculiar outcome of the chemical reactions and inter-reactions that take place within the physical body. If this is the case, then how is it that each individual is able to entertain different ideas and views on the general subjects of everyday existence? Furthermore, if, as this theory leads us to believe, we are all the result of some chemical formulation, then surely those who adhere to it, aided by the latest advances in technology and understanding of the body's biochemistry, would have created a chemical formula which, when injected into a corpse, would bring it back to life! The fact that they have not appears to confirm the view that when the purpose of spirit has departed from the physical body, a certain cycle is complete and death results. This latter view perceives the purpose or spirit as the driving force of life, and the physical body as no more than the vehicle for its expression.

The same principle applies on a larger scale to the universe, for it, too, has purpose – a purpose which expresses itself through universal order, and through the measurable cycles of linear time in the seasons and the movement of the planets. However, this universal order is not entirely clockwork, behaving like some vast machine incapable of thought. The uncertainty or 'chaos' principle reminds us of that, keeping us guessing (and learning) about the purposeful 'whole' of which we are an intrinsic part.

We have already considered that people are born at a particular time, sharing with those born under the same astrological sign certain characteristics that differ from those born under others. Additionally, some are born in one country, some in another, into different families with specific genetic tendencies. In one sense it could be said that we have chosen these ourselves, but not in the sense that the personality we refer to as 'you' and 'I' has chosen them. They are chosen by the element of purpose for which our physical body is the vehicle so that we may fulfil the purpose for which we come into the world. It would thus appear that we can choose to respond to the events occurring in our lives from one of two levels – the one is from the level of purpose, corresponding to our deeper sense of universal purpose; the other is from the more localized level of our personality. This freedom of choice can be regarded as the element of free will. Our response then in any given situation is not unlike the uncertainty principle, for we can never predetermine precisely how we will act or react as the situation unfolds and other elements come into play. In that respect life is very much like a school or university, and each of life's experiences provides us with an opportunity to learn whatever we need to learn about the purposeful whole of which we are a part.

In the light of these last statements we can say that, in one sense or the other, a patient chooses his or her own experience, whether this is to do with their career, environment or state of health and that if things begin to go wrong, he or she also has the choice of how to deal with the situation in which they find themselves. If this is the case, why is there an apparent need for outside medical help or counselling? The reason is that there are times when the patient becomes submerged by outside interference in the form of external influences of an inimical nature, or incorrect thought processes, and he or she loses the ability to organize things for themselves. As we are all ultimately sharing in the same purpose it is quite natural for them to turn for help and receive it from their fellow human beings. In this respect the role of a physician also carries with it a responsibility as educator and, where many of today's illnesses are concerned, the required remedy is more to do with re-education than remedial work at a purely physical level.

One may also ask why, if life is an educational process, is illness sometimes a necessary part of the process? Illness arises from an imbalance of the equation purpose = mind = body (or, spirit = mind = matter). According to most metaphysical and religious teachings, all life on earth emanates from the spirit or universal purpose (or its similarly named equivalent). Therefore if the dimension of spirit or purpose has chosen to express itself via a particular experience or path in life, it has to see it through to its completion. At an energetic level this dimension is the continual flow of life force which, by energizing and directing the mind, expresses itself in the tangible physical world. If, for one reason or another, this flow of energy becomes blocked, imbalance and disharmony will result. Here again, the patient is faced with a choice of action regarding the situation in which they find themselves.

In previous chapters we have examined the basic causative factors of ill health. From these few factors arise thousands of different conditions which develop into acute or chronic ill-nesses. Acute illnesses affect the physical body directly and, being of a shorter duration, will not return if the correct remedies are given. They are often nothing more than early warnings of something at a deeper level which, if not corrected, may turn into a chronic long-term disorder. The repeated occurrence of irritating acute conditions therefore stems from a deeper, or more chronic, underlying cause. Continuous reinfection of the physical body in this manner requires investigation at the level of mental attitudes and consciousness for deficiencies in the immune system are clearly indicated.

Irritating illnesses are often linked to autointoxication factors such as poisons and toxins from the oral cavity due to sensitivity to the amalgam used in dental fillings, or 'strep' and 'staph' infections that continually focus on the tonsils or tonsil stubs, polluting the bloodstream and causing toxaemia. Ileo-caecal valve syndrome is also prevalent today, causing similar symp-toms to amalgam poisoning such as major bowel problems, nausea, faintness, pain around the heart, and dark circles under the eyes. ICV syndrome can occur equally from an open or closed valve. An open valve allows waste products to filter back into the small intestine thus allowing toxicity to arise via the intestinal wall, whereas a closed valve results in the food being held for too long in the small intestine, leading to the food putrefying and becoming toxic. Meat eaters can have a particularly bad time from this type of toxicity. ICV often emanates from muscle spasm, stress or emotional troubles, all of which are experienced via the solar plexus energy centre.

Chronic illness manifests over a long period, often building from acute or irritating illnesses to a state of atrophy or immobility. It also brings with it a certain consciousness and attitude(s) that patients are obliged to recognize and face, if they wish to obtain any kind of remission. For this reason illnesses of this nature need to be looked at with depth and reasoning in order for the causative factor to be effectively identified, isolated and treated. The cause may be traced to any one or more of a number of considerations, including hereditary influence, stress, psychosomatic disorders, and congested mental or emotional states. In the process of identifying the cause, patients probably need to look back into their past to recollect the thought processes that surfaced at the onset of illness or, in some cases, even further back. Negative reactions such as anger, frustration or emotional stress in response to a shock, bad news of some kind, or the loss of a job, may prove to have played a causative role. How could we possibly avoid such reactions when, for example, we see a loved one severely injured in front of our eyes?

In the course of our daily lives, shocks to the system at one level or another are largely unavoidable. When these happen it is important to face the situation exactly as it is. A perfectly harmless emotional outburst at the time may be a natural part of the process of acknowledging and accepting what has taken place, but if we allow ourselves to indulge in feelings of guilt, blame and resentment, or even pretend that nothing has happened at all, we are simply storing up trouble for ourselves in the long term. Often it is the aftermath of the experience and the way we handle it that brings the self-limiting thoughts that affect our bodily functions and then bring about the onset of illness or disease. It is therefore important to realize that we cannot hide from the experiences of life by making excuses for ourselves, or holding others responsible for our apparent misfortunes, for to do so is to impair the flow of life-giving energy.

I have had patients who have improved tremendously just by recognizing the causative factor of their illness and by coming to terms with the experience it brought them. And, of course, the release from illness or its successful treatment brings with it the resumption of life's flow, frequently resulting in the patient developing a new awareness of their environment and a progressive outlook on life. Out of this awareness comes joy, for the two go hand in hand. In fact, many individuals have been prodded out of their spiritual lethargy by the profound experience that a major illness or disease wreaking havoc in their physical body can bring. In a number of these cases the change in thinking and conscious attitudes engendered by spiritual upliftment has served to further heal the physical body.

CHAPTER 7

To the Next Dimension

One important step for the future of medicine lies in a willingness for orthodox and complementary practitioners to understand the methods practised by each other in their respective quests to heal patients and prevent disease. In that regard, the complementary practitioner who refuses to acknowledge what conventional medical practice has to offer is as unenlightened as his or her orthodox counterpart who dismisses all aspects of complementary medicine out of hand. Patients can and should be helped by both methods, and the time is now ripe for all of us who see our function as effectively curing illness and disease to recognize our common purpose and work together for the benefit of our patients. After all, the effective and progressive healing of the whole individual is as much a process of expansion and development for the medical practitioner as it is for the patient.

In describing the various elements that go to make up the biomedical model, considerable emphasis has been placed on the role of the energetic dimension of thought and the multi-dimensional sphere of its activity, from the level of subatomic particles to that of the universal mind. In fact, within the space-time continuum proposed by quantum physics, there are no limits to the dimension of thought except those imposed by the minds of individuals. Here, too, we have an important factor to take into account when envisaging the medicine of the future, for the prime cause of illness lies in the restrictions placed by the individual personality on the free flow of purposeful thought from the universal mind.

'MIND STUFF'

The potential to utilize thought for healing within the continuum of space-time has already been employed by radionics practitioners for some years now as well as by, in more recent times, a number of forward-thinking orthodox physicians. In order to understand a little more about the way in which this 'thought' or 'mind' medicine works, we need to take a brief look at some of the ideas and theories currently expressed by quantum physicists, especially with regard to the shadowy world where energy and matter are different dimensions of what is, to all intents and purposes, a single phenomenon.

The transformational relationship between matter and energy was proven succinctly by Einstein's mass-energy equation, $E=mc^2$, thus enabling the mind of the physicist to break through the barrier that had previously separated the two scientifically. It also opened the way for the quantum physicists to identify and investigate the elementary particles of energetic matter that are the fundamental units of the material universe (including, of course, human beings). Amongst the smallest of these quantum units is the *quark* which is so small that it hovers across the very boundary between the visible and invisible worlds, and the point at which the difference of state between mass and energy/particle and wave is barely discernible. But what lies beyond the quark? Here the physicist at present has little more to add, except to say that perhaps there is some invisible reality that is totally non-material, described, appropriately, as *virtual* reality. It is in this pre-physical world of virtual reality that the minds and ideas of the physicist and the metaphysical philosopher meet.

'The world was born out of invisible perfect forms and geometric shapes.' At least, that was how Plato saw it. Perhaps we can relate his perception to our own understanding of the universe and, more specifically, the world in which we live. In one sense our view of the world is nothing but impulses carried up and down the various channels of the nervous system to the brain. In turn these impulses come from the energetic vibrations (light, sound, etc.) existing outside our nervous system but within our environment. On which of these do we base our understanding of reality – the impulses within our central nervous system, or the vibrations in space, or a combination of both? Or is it that reality, like the quark, hovers between the visible and invisible? In other words, energy (and therefore matter), at its finest level, is nothing more than encoded thoughts ('the invisible perfect forms') emanating from the universal mind which, when perceived by an observer, are brought into being. And where, one may well ask, does the observer come from? Here again quantum physics and metaphysics intermingle. As far as quantum physics is concerned the observer is a necessary part of the experiment for without him or her the experiment cannot take place, while metaphysics tells us that the universal mind thinks itself into being in order to see itself.

We encounter a similar phenomenon in the world of symbols. Humanity uses symbols to represent formal constructs. On receipt of the symbol the mind of the 'observer' (at a directly conscious level or at a deeper level of the subconscious) visualizes the actual form or construct the symbol represents. In other words, the symbol acts as an impulse of coded instruction. This is the concept of mind medicine as used in the Base 64 instrument. Specially constructed symbols are transmitted as energetic seed thoughts or impulses and, operating at a quantum level within a space-time continuum they are able to transcend the boundaries of the coarser physical space-time reality we normally perceive.

The function of mind medicine, where the relationship between the patient and practitioner is concerned, is best summed up by the phrase 'two minds are better than one'. Let's explain this by saying that if the practitioner can ascertain at a mind level from the patient's blueprint the purpose and aspirations of the patient, and the patient has mindfully asked to be healed, then the practitioner's understanding of the cause of the patient's illness will be transmitted to the patient as encoded thought energy at a mind level so that the necessary healing can take place.

I have conducted this as an experiment many times by administering a placebo medication while, at the same time, holding the cause of the patient's illness in my mind and using symbols on certain predesigned cards in the Base 64 light-activated instrument. The symbolic pattern used is designed specifically from the patient's blueprint and, because the blueprint (like the physical 'genetic fingerprint') is unique, the transmission of encoded thought can only influence the causal mind of that particular patient. If we refer back to the case history of Rose (see p. 145), the sequence of cards inserted in the instrument would be activated by the controlled flashing of photons of light through the central aperture of the cards. The last card carries the encoded vital essence of Rose and so the entire imprint of symbolic thought is transmitted through the space-time continuum to the mind of the person whose vital essence corresponds to the encoded message – in this case Rose – and nobody else. In this respect, mind medicine takes us beyond radionics to a yet more subtle dimension of 'action at a distance', because radionics necessitates the practitioner's use of a 'witness' (for instance, a lock of hair) from the patient.

Patients and other interested parties have sometimes expressed a degree of concern regarding the safety of healing at this extended dimension. In the same way that there is, for example, a universal law of 'cause equals effect' there is also a universal law that applies to the quantum dimension of healing: namely, the patient must grant permission, consciously or subconsciously, for healing to occur before the *probable* acceptance of the encoded thought by the patient can take place. (In quantum physics, this is referred to as the uncertainty principle, i.e. not all proposed actions are guaranteed). A further safety factor with this dimension of healing is that the practitioner can very rarely make a mistake that will have an adverse effect on the patient. The reason for this is that the equation of 'purpose = mind = body' means that if the practitioner transmits an incorrectly coded thought, the patient's dimension of purpose will override the instruction.

THE FUTURE FOR A THREE-DIMENSIONAL MODEL

As the saying goes, 'Time alone will tell'. Over the last four years I have explained the Base 64 system to many physicians and health care professionals and the results and comments that have come back to me have been more than encouraging. This book will, I trust, make for further understanding regarding the potential of healing at this dimension, leading to further experimentation that will be of benefit to the medicine of the future. The wider acceptance of a new biological model is, of course, hampered by the strong divisions that exist between orthodox medical practice and complementary medicine but, nevertheless, the system outlined here can be used by both. Hopefully, it may also serve to further a joint understanding between quantum physics and biology by providing them with a common ground and purpose.

As previously stated, current thinking in biology gives little credence to the mind of matter. The medicine of the future will, I believe, have to take notice of the elements of mind and purpose within cells because cell memory, or the *endergonic process*, which passes from cell to cell during normal cellular metabolism, provides the ongoing link for both the DNA and mind element of cells. The mind element of cells, which I believe contains the blueprint for the individual, passes into each cell the memory of all past events experienced during the individual's lifetime. I am sure many readers have experienced the physical memory of a symptom when suddenly remembering a past trauma or anxiety. This phenomenon can be explained by the presence of cell memory, a memory bank within each cell that will bring to the forefront of the individual's consciousness a mental or physical symptom when a similar event or thought sparks off the endergonic process.

During our lifetime the three-dimensional model is at work within us, the purpose factor striving to influence the mind and body via the desired aspirations encoded in the vital essence or blueprint. Of course, we can also express our free will by choosing to accept or reject our true purpose in life. This is the main cause of illness as the correct functioning of both the immune and organ systems are disturbed due to the breakdown of the individual's organizing electromagnetic field. By rejecting our purpose or desired aspiration we set up a negative reaction and healing can then only be truly successful when the energetic flow of the purpose factor is properly restored. In this overview of our model it is important to remember that the mind can also be affected by local environmental factors which then influence both the purpose and body. The model thus provides an equation for good health that looks like this:

$$\text{PURPOSE} \longleftrightarrow \text{MIND} \longleftrightarrow \text{BODY}$$

Influence from all three elements can pass in both directions. When the influence travels from right to left (that is, from body and mind into the purpose factor) this provides *karma* for the coming months or years or, in the case of terminal illness, for the next dimension, passing the information into the '0' symbol or *Daath* (see Appendix 3).

In the years I have been using the system it has become apparent to me that disease will often manifest in areas of weakness in the physical body; that is, in areas of aspiration. If an aspiration contained in the blueprint is not fulfilled, the energy centre no longer performs at its optimum. This means that the lowered flow of vital energy emanating from it is not strong enough to prevent invasion by virus or bacteria, because the necessary degree of corrective influence is not available in that area. The teleological process requires the presence of the purpose factor for the immune system and the structural molecular procedures of DNA (production of amino acids, proteins, biochemistry, and so on) to function correctly in tandem.

The individual's own blueprint of purpose and health, which is at the heart of the Base 64 system, provides the following:

1.   An insight into the aspirations and purpose of the patient's life – that is, the effects of purpose on mind and body.
2.   The possibility for the physician to trace the cause of a patient's illness by noting the location of the symptoms and relating them to the corresponding energy centre, category or attendant meridian – that is, the effects of mind on body.
3.   The recognition of the effects that physically invasive drug therapy and environmental toxins or poisons will have on the mental or emotional levels of the individuals – that is, the effects of body on mind.
4.   Previously unknown mind level causes for a patient's illness.
5.   The strengths and weaknesses of a patient's biochemistry and organ systems, and allow physical material remedies to be administered to promote the strengths.
6.   Where younger patients are concerned, it enables the practitioner to prepare and consult charts of both parents in order to obtain a clearer picture of genetic influence on the patient's biochemic strengths and weaknesses.
7.   The possibility for the physician to trace non-local causes by using the meridian flow system.
8.   A blueprint of the electromagnetic field surrounding the individual's physical body and the microcosmic pattern existing endergonically in every cell.

9.   When used as part of the diagnostic procedure, the system will assist those physicians working with material remedies in general practice and those complementary practitioners who use subtle energetic medicine.

The principal aim of the Base 64 blueprint is to provide an understanding of the purposeful dimension of life and to give it a tangible dimension of expression which is meaningful for each of us, whether in good or ill health. This dimension of purpose or causation provides a vital component in the biomedical model for the twenty-first century. In constructing the Base 64 system and its blueprint, I have been conscious of the dangers of producing yet another 'system' that creates a rigidity of thought arising from the sense of obligation, whether stated overtly or merely implied, that those who use it should strictly adhere to it. In that sense, Base 64 is not a system so much as a synthesis of current knowledge assembled in such a way that it should be acceptable, at least in part, to most people (whether practitioners, patients or simply interested individuals) who care about the human race, its health and its potential. The material contained in this book can be used by the reader as a whole or in part and it is my sincere hope that the reader will feel free to use the various elements described in whatever manner they feel appropriate in their search for health, happiness and purposeful fulfilment in their lives.

In broader terms the Base 64 approach to medicine should be acceptable to both Western and Eastern thinking as well as to the different branches of science and philosophy that proliferate in both schools of thought. At a time in history when divisiveness and confrontation abound, and when personal interests and material gain are so often placed before the wider good, there is a need for humanity to unify its thoughts and ideals in order to ensure its future well-being. That is why the material contained within these pages stands centrally between West and East, physics and metaphysics, biology and cosmology, allopathic and complementary medicine, and science and religion. The author trusts that it will be received in this spirit and that those who read it will enjoy it as much as a journey of self-discovery as a blueprint for the medicine of the twenty-first century.

Glossary of Terms

Some of these terms are defined in a way that is specific to my system of working.

Alta Major: Energy centre at the base of the occiput.

Ameliorate: To make or become better.

Antimatter: Also known as shadow matter. The electromagnetic field surrounding the matter which occupies space in the visible world. The formative dimension of matter.

Anthropic: A theory which suggests that we as observers have, by our very presence, selected a region of space-time with perceptible dimensions. We could not live in any other differently dimensional domain which may exist.

Aspiration: Purpose with objective intention.

Autointoxication: Self-poisoning caused by toxic products originating within the body.

Ayurveda: An holistic medical system of India.

Biochemistry: The study of chemical compounds and reactions occurring in living organisms.

Blueprint: Original causality containing objective information.

Category: Accumulation of the varying characteristics of an individual. Used diagnostically with regard to a particular energy centre or gland.

Causal: Primary stimulant for causation of form.

Ch'i: Vital energy flowing along meridians, as understood in Chinese philosophy.

Complementary: Interdependant and mutually acceptable.

Daath: *See* Appendix 3.

DNA: Deoxyribonucleic acid.

Demulcent: Soothing and bland.

Diuretic: Medicine to stimulate the flow of urine.

Elemental: Unmodified original essence.

Energy Centre (or Thought Centre): Synonymous with Category, in this context.

Endergonic process: The absorption or input of free energy (see p. 18).

Endocrine gland: Gland which secretes hormones directly into the blood stream.

Epinephrine: Adrenaline. A hormone secreted by the adrenal medulla, often released during the fight or flight mechanism and in response to hypoglycaemia.

EPR experiment: Einstein–Podolski–Rosen experiment (see p. 73).

Essence: Essential living being, the vitality of living form.

Force field: Electromagnetic energy surrounding living form.

Hexagram: An arrangement of six lines, either broken (Yin) or unbroken (Yang), constituting possible combinations of cosmic archetypes.

Hypoglycaemia: Low blood sugar.

Irradiation: Application of radiant energy (heat, light, roentgen ray, radium etc). Can be used for therapeutic and diagnostic purposes.

Karma: Forces of creation from which all things have their origin.

Mentation: The process or result of mental activity.

Meridian: In Chinese philosophy, a pathway along which ch'i or free energy passes.

Meridian (Subtle Meridian or Thought String): Used in this book to refer to the pathway of energy between the Energy or Thought Centres.

Metaphysics: A branch of philosophy which deals with the nature of existence, truth and knowledge.

Mitochondria: The principle site within a cell of oxidative reactions by which the energy of foodstuffs is made available.

Palliative: A substance given to relieve symptoms.

Placebo: Inactive substance given in place of medicine.

Polarity: Condition of having poles exhibiting opposite effects.

Pronuclei: The nuclei of mature ovum and spermatozoa before fertilization.

QED: Quantum Electro Dynamics.

Quantum Theory: A theory concerning the behaviour of physical systems based on the idea that they can only possess certain properties, such as energy, in discrete amounts (quanta).

Reincarnation: A theory of life, death and rebirth which suggests that on the death of the physical body the 'soul' is born again in another body.

Simulate: To reproduce similar conditions or effects.

Subtle Energy: Energy of a fine nature, difficult to detect or analyze, and needing active perception for interpretation.

Taoism: A form of Chinese philosophy and self-cultivation. Many parallels have been drawn between the ideas of Taoism and modern physics.

Universal Mind: A mind of omnipotent, unlimited power, knowing of all things.

Yin and Yang: The archetypal and complementary aspects of absolute knowledge within Chinese philosophy. A fundamental division of forces into opposites, eg. female–male, dark–light, yielding–aggressive, etc.

Appendix 1

The following dates are for use in conjunction with Figure 6 on p. 36.

Aries   March 21st to April 19th
Taurus   April 20th to May 20th
Gemini   May 21st to June 21st
Cancer   June 22nd to July 22nd
Leo   July 23rd to August 22nd
Virgo   August 23rd to September 22nd
Libra   September 23rd to October 23rd
Scorpio   October 24th to November 21st
Sagittarius November 22nd to December 21st
Capricorn   December 22nd to January 19th
Aquarius   January 20th to February 18th
Pisces   February 19th to March 20th

Appendix 2

The following table shows the celloid minerals that correspond to the nine categories of the blueprint formula described in Chapter 2. A patient's weaknesses at a physical or energetic level may be strengthened by the use of these celloid minerals with their respective categories. Symptoms occurring in the areas governed by these numerical categories will be improved by the use of the associated celloid mineral, even in those situations when the symptoms may not provide an exact match. When treating symptoms in this way we are making use of the energetic aspect of the mineral at a formative level.

Category 1 Magnesium Phosphate (MP 65)
Category 2 Iron Phosphate (IP 82), Silica (S 79)
Category 3 Calcium Sulphate (CS 36), Potassium Phosphate (PP 85)
Category 4 Calcium Fluoride (CF 43)
Category 5 Potassium Chloride (PC 73), Potassium Sulphate (PS 29)
Category 6 Calcium Phosphate (CP 57)
Category 7 Sodium Phosphate (SP 96), Sodium Sulphate (SS 69)
Category 8 Calcium Phosphate (CP 57), Iron Phosphate (IP 82)
Category 9 Calcium Phosphate (CP 57)

Further information on mineral celloids (colloidal minerals) is available from: Blackmores Laboratories Ltd.,
             Unit 7, Poyle Tech Centre,
             Willow Road, Colnbrook,
             Bucks (England)

Appendix 3 Daath

According to some esoteric teachings Daath corresponds to our true will and ultimate purpose in life. In the context of this book, it is regarded as something that we need to contact and understand on a moment-to-moment basis in our daily lives. At a further, macrocosmic dimension of humanity, I consider Daath to be the dimension into which we pass at the end of this life, for the purpose and will that gave us form must move on at the moment of death (perhaps there is even a subtle connection between the two words death and Daath). Others may refer to Daath as being the eleventh, or hidden, sphere on the Tree of Life.

Interestingly enough, the Meridian 22 which leads from Daath to Centre 9 is a seed thought of progression to higher attainment and the completion of a cycle. At a microcosmic level, this corresponds to the endergonic process by which the genetic and purpose factors are passed on from the dying cell to its replacement. At the macrocosmic level, the blueprint supplies the vital life plan or accumulated karma of this life to the next dimension of life, where it is perhaps assessed by the Great Architect of the universe on whose decision it either passes on to a higher realm or reassumes physical form in order to fulfil its purpose and aspiration at the level of this world.

A further interesting possibility of the blueprint is to compile a formula for the individual at the point of death. The process is the same as that used in connection with the point of conception and birth (including the maiden name of a married woman) except that the details of dates and sometimes countries are changed. Comparison between the two charts allows one to see whether the individual has attained the desired purpose and aspiration, and whether the weaknesses have been converted into strengths.

Further Reading

The following is a short list of highly readable books, some of which have been used as sources of reference for material in the preceding pages, that are recommended reading for those who wish to further their interest in the thinking behind the medicine of the future.

Augros, R. and Stanciu, G. *The New Biology*, Shambhala, 1987.

Bailey, A. *Esoteric Psychology – Volume 2*, Lucis Press, 1942.

Barrow, J. and Tipler, F. *The Anthropic Cosmological Principle*, Oxford University Press, 1988.

Capra, F. *The Turning Point*, Simon & Schuster, 1982.

Chopra, D. *Quantum Healing*, Bantam, 1989.

Davies, P. *Superforce*, Unwin Paperbacks, 1984.

Davies, P. *The Cosmic Blueprint*, Simon & Schuster/Touchstone, 1989.

Dossey, L. *Recovering the Soul*, Bantam, 1989.

Hawking, S. *A Brief History of Time*, Bantam, 1988.

Parfitt, W. *The Living Qabalah*, Element Books, 1988.

Peat, F. David, *Superstrings and the Search for the Theory of Everything*, Sphere Books Ltd, 1991.

Roberts, H. A. *The Principles and Art of Cure by Homoeopathy*, Health Science Press, 1936..

Sawtell, V. *Astrology and Biochemistry*, Health Science Press, 1947.

Vines, G. Test tube embryos. *New Scientist*, 19.11.1987.

Useful Addresses

For additional information on the Base 64 System and treatment instruments, or regarding lectures and seminars, contact:

> Keith Mason, The Old Chapel, Bodenham, Salisbury, Wiltshire SP5 4EU

For health assessments and interpretation of blueprints the author may be contacted at the above address.

For general information on complementary medicine write to:

> The Institute For Complementary Medicine,
> P.O. Box 194
> London SE16 1QZ

Index